### Fire Protection Association

# FIRE RISK MANAGEMENT IN THE WORKPLACE
## A Guide for Employers

Third edition
Adair Lewis and William Dailey

**FIRE PROTECTION ASSOCIATION**

First edition: 1997
Second edition: May 2000
Third edition: June 2006
Reprinted edition: October 2008

The Fire Protection Association
London Road, Moreton in Marsh, Gloucestershire GL56 0RH
© Fire Protection Association 2008

ISBN 1 902790 40 5

Reprinted by Lightning Source, Milton Keynes

# Contents

# **1** Introduction

The term 'risk management' has, over recent years, started to appear more prominently in the fire safety managers' vocabulary and continues for some to fill them with horror and foreboding. Yet another complex technical subject to get to grips with and to have to explain to the bosses? Yet another weapon to be used by enforcing authorities? More time being needlessly spent to satisfy faceless bureaucrats?

No – the truth is very different. We have all been assessing risks since we were in our childhood: perhaps the risk of jumping from an ever increasing number of stairs, or the risk of acquiring another chocolate biscuit without getting caught. As times change so the risks in our lives have changed. In crossing a road or overtaking when driving, a risk assessment is made. It may only take a brief second, but it will involve the same type of process as do the risk assessments that are now required to be undertaken in the workplace. Health and safety risk assessments have had to be undertaken for some time but it is only since 1997 that fire risks have also had to be assessed in the UK as part of the Fire Precautions (Workplace) Regulations 1997 as amended by the Fire Precautions (Workplace) (Amendment) Regulations 1999. The legal background to risk assessments is described in Chapter 2.

The aim of this publication is to take the mystery out of risk assessments, in particular fire risk assessments that have been required in almost every place of work by the Fire Precautions (Workplace) Regulations 1997 (as amended) and are a core requirement of the Regulatory Reform (Fire Safety) Order 2005, in force from 1 October 2006. In all but the most complex of workplaces the fire safety manager should be capable of carrying out assessments to satisfy the legal requirements; only in exceptional cases will assistance have to be sought from outside specialists.

It is likely that only a minimal amount of work will be necessary following the risk assessment. Fire safety managers who are undertaking the exercise for the first time may well be surprised to find that they have been unconsciously carrying out the process for several months, or even years. It should be remembered, though, that legislation sets out minimum standards of fire protection and consideration should be given to enhancing this level when planning installations or management procedures.

Many people may think that risk assessment and risk management are terms that only relate to major disasters. This is not necessarily the case, a small fire can, in some cases, cause a company to cease trading but in other circumstances a major fire might easily be survived.

## What is a disaster?

A disaster is different according to the prevailing circumstances. Officially, as far as national and local government are concerned a disaster is:

'any unwanted significant incident which threatens personnel, buildings, or the operational structure of an organisation, which requires special measures to be taken to restore things back to normal.' (*How resilient is your business to disaster?*, Home Office, 1997.)

Everyone assumes that they would recognise a disaster when they see one – or would they? Clearly the crash of a wide-bodied passenger aircraft on a small Scottish town falls into everyone's idea of a disaster, but what about less obvious examples? Is a fire in a power station a disaster? It will probably demand a substantial fire brigade response and some urgent management decisions will be needed in the various national and regional control rooms to ensure that as few consumers as possible are inconvenienced. But, in a UK context, it would not be classified as a disaster. What would happen in a small island state where there is only one power station? Is that a disaster? It almost certainly is as the impact on the population would be substantial and, depending on the degree of damage, it may be a very long time before supplies are returned to normal.

So one of the first lessons of disaster management is that the definition of disaster will be different for each organisation. Thus, in general terms:

'A disaster is any unlooked-for incident threatening the personnel, buildings, or normal operational structure of an organisation which is beyond the immediate ability of the organisation's staff and normal management structure to control.'

This definition would be equally suited to a major flood, fire, bomb threat or even an influx of vermin.

## Risk assessment and hazard analysis

Having defined a disaster, let us try to predict just what we need to prepare for. Obviously one of the most significant things about disasters is that they cannot (normally) be predicted. If we knew when fire or accident was likely to strike, we could take precautions!

What we can do is to attempt to assess the possible or likely range of incidents which any given premises is liable to suffer and then try to rate these according to probability. A specific threat matrix for businesses can be simply constructed taking the risks in descending order of severity:

| Risk Factor | Probability | Consequence |
|---|---|---|
| Earthquake | Very Low | Disastrous |
| Bomb | Low | Disastrous |
| Arson | Low | Disastrous |
| Accidental fire | Low | Disastrous |
| Flood | Medium | Disastrous |
| Robbery | Low | Problematic |
| Theft | Medium | Loss of item |
| Vandalism | High | Extra work, cost |
| Assault | High | Staff morale |

*Figure 1.1. The probability and consequences of selected disasters*

Thus, while it is clear that an earthquake, crashing jumbo jet or any other remote possibility is almost certainly the most damaging event, it is also the least likely. While vandalism or assault are much higher probabilities, their impact on the organisation (but not necessarily on individuals) is likely to be much lower.

The conclusion to be drawn from all this is that fire, flood and bombs are credible risks with high enough probability scores to keep the average managing director awake at least one night of the week.

## Risk assessment and the laws of chance

Let's look at the chance of an event occurring in another way. A coin, when tossed, can land heads or tails uppermost, thus the chance of tossing heads or tails is one in two. But if you toss a coin and it lands heads six times in succession what is the chance of the next toss being heads? The answer is exactly the same, one in two. In a similar way a couple expecting a baby may end up with either a boy or a girl, a chance of one in two, ignoring any genetic influences. The odds of having 10 boys in a row are 1 in 1024 but what are the odds of the next child being a boy?

The answer is that the odds of completing the football team is still one in two. To put it another way, there is no law of chance – but there may be readers who want to contradict this statement, based on the fact that a piece of buttered toast, if dropped, will always land butter side down!

The *consequences* of an event bear no relation at all to the likelihood of that event occurring. A one in six chance is often regarded as more advantageous than a one in a million chance but the consequences of playing Russian roulette are much more serious than winning the National Lottery.

In considering the cause of a fire, there are some circumstances when the risk is so high that a fire is bound to occur. A spillage of low flash point solvent in the immediate vicinity of a flame *will* result in a fire occurring, this is not an exercise in probability theory. But if a cigarette stub is dropped into a bin containing paper a fire will not always occur. The likelihood of a fire resulting depends on the amount of tobacco left to smoulder in the stub, the orientation of the cigarette, the type of material on which it lands and the ventilation. This is too complex to quantify but we know that in the right circumstances (or some would say the wrong circumstances) a fire can occur.

One thing is for certain, however, and that is that if a large number of cigarettes are thrown into bins containing paper then a fire will, sooner or later, occur. It may be difficult to put a numerical value on the probability of it happening in a certain period of time but it only needs to happen once to have repercussions serious enough to put the company out of business. Therefore all possible causes of ignition, including the practice of smoking, need to be addressed in some way.

Although it is not possible to give an absolute value to a risk, there are several methods which may be used to rate a risk as being of low, normal or high level, or to give some numerical rating to the risk which may be used when comparing survey results from various areas; these are described in Chapter 3.

## What a risk assessment involves

The purpose of a risk assessment is not necessarily to quantify the risks that are present in the workplace but to identify them and then to:

- eliminate;
- control;
- avoid;
- transfer; or
- accept the risks.

In carrying out the fire risk assessment it may be helpful to consider the five main factors which should be taken into account:

- *People:* their number, location, age and state of mind.

- *Use of the building:* the nature of the work that is being undertaken and the materials involved.

- *Furnishings:* the type and nature of the furniture, curtains, carpets etc that are present.

- *Finishes:* the presence of surface finishes which could cause the rapid build up of heat and smoke.

- *Structures:* the presence of unsatisfactory structural features.

Identifying fire hazards in the workplace and measures that can be taken to reduce them are described in Chapter 4.

Following this exercise, consideration must be given to coping with the residual risks that are an inherent part of the company's business. These must be addressed by providing effective escape routes and the installation of fire protection systems such as fire alarms, emergency escape lighting and firefighting equipment. These measures are described in Chapter 5.

Escape routes and fire protection equipment do not look after themselves and thus management action is necessary to ensure that the escape routes are always available for immediate use whenever people are at work in a building and to keep fire protection equipment serviced and maintained so that it will work efficiently when required. Staff also need to react correctly and efficiently in an emergency and thus staff training is also a key element of the measures described in Chapter 6.

In every building, even those with a low risk of a fire occurring, there should be fire wardens appointed by a fire safety manager. This manager also has responsibility for drawing up the fire action notices and procedures which form the basis of staff training. This is the subject of Chapter 7.

Chapter 8 deals with a relatively new risk that is increasingly encountered – the threat from arson and terrorism. The incidence of arson has increased to the extent that it now accounts for over 40% of all fires and the monetary cost of this crime is estimated to be in excess of £1m per day. Other costs of arson include consequential losses to company continuity and profits and the loss of amenities to the public as well as damage to the environment. Although terrorist attacks are much rarer, the consequences resulting from a single attack can be very much greater.

In very small businesses the only emergency plan that is produced is the fire action notice that is circulated to staff or displayed next to the fire alarm call points. In most businesses, however, a more far-reaching plan is needed, not only to ensure that all staff escape from a fire without injury, but also to ensure that damage to property is kept to a minimum and that the business can reopen with the minimum of down time. Planning for emergencies is the subject of Chapter 10.

Finally, a rather more specialist subject makes up the last chapter of this book. Planning to minimise the acid smoke hazard is discussed in Chapter 11. Although it is widely appreciated that it is the smoke from a fire, rather than the flames, that poses the greater threat to life, it is because the smoke often contains significant quantities of acidic gases such as hydrogen chloride, that it also represents a serious threat to property. This is particularly so when acidic smoke comes into contact with precision engineered parts and electronic circuit boards which are present in many items, especially machine tools and computers.

The appendices list the areas where the Regulatory Reform (Fire Safety) Order 2005 does not apply, provide checklists to be used in conjunction with Chapter 4 and a list of addresses that readers may find useful. The fire risk assessment checklists can also be used in conjunction with the FPA's *Workplace Fire Safety Log Book* in order to ensure that your staff and your company are as safe as possible from the effects of fire.

**Practical solutions**

When the 'risk assessment approach' was first introduced with the implementation of the Fire Precautions (Workplace) Regulations, the intention was that it should have a minimal impact on business finance. This was because it was thought that the majority of fire protection measures would already have been implemented in sectors of industry and commerce where fire safety has been taken seriously. In some companies, however, particularly smaller ones, this may not have been the case and in these instances financial provision will have to be made.

While many companies may choose to make the minimum provisions to protect their staff and property in the event of fire, others may be tempted to adopt a 'belt and braces' approach, perhaps with the addition of a length of string for good measure. The optimum solution, however, will be one that is cost effective and even so it has to be realised that the solution will almost certainly not completely eliminate the chances of a fire occurring, but will reduce it to a level commensurate with the nature of the business that is being undertaken. As indicated in Figure 1.2, this is normally a balancing act, ensuring that the precautions that are taken are appropriate to the inherent

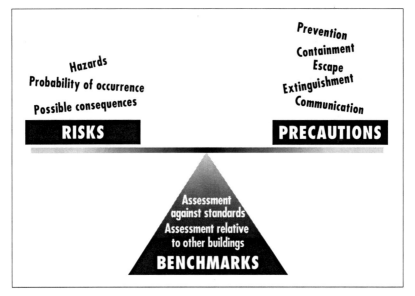

*Figure 1.2 The cost effective balancing act*

risk and that the solutions that are adopted acknowledge the relevant standards and the lessons learnt from fires that have occurred in similar premises in the past.

Finally, a risk assessment is not a one-off exercise, but one that needs to be reviewed and updated regularly.

# The legal background to fire risk assessment

## The Fire Precautions Act 1971

The concept of fire risk assessment is not new. The fire safety arrangements in places of work such as factories, offices, shops, and railway premises, hotels and boarding houses (otherwise known as 'designated premises') were for many years dictated by the provisions of the Fire Precautions Act 1971. This required the owner or occupier of a factory, office, shop or railway premises where the number of people at work exceeded certain numerical limits, to apply for and maintain a fire certificate. Similar numerical limits were prescribed for hotels and boarding houses but were related to the provision of sleeping accommodation. The coming into force of the Regulatory Reform (Fire Safety) Order 2005 on 1 October 2006 resulted in the Fire Precautions Act ceasing to have effect and hence existing fire certificates no longer being valid. However, for the purposes of this chapter it is worth looking back at the requirements of the Fire Precautions Act – albeit briefly.

The Home Office issued its *Guide to Fire Precautions in Existing Places of Work that require a Fire Certificate; Factories, Offices, Shops and Railway Premises*. The purpose of this guide – colloquially known as the 'blue book' – was to set out reasonable standards of means of escape and other fire precautions in existing premises that required a fire certificate. Part II of the guide was directed primarily at the fire authorities that were responsible for issuing fire certificates under the Fire Precautions Act 1971, and Chapter 13 within this was called 'Assessment of Fire Risk and Associated Life Risk'. This chapter described the factors that needed to be considered in order to determine the level of risk, thus 'enabling adoption of the appropriate fire precautions'. Furthermore, Chapter 13 talked about the *level* of risk and gave quite lengthy definitions of low, normal and high fire risk. To give one example of the way in which the assessed level or category of fire risk determines the corresponding level of fire precautions, the guide specified, for the various categories of fire risk, the maximum permissible travel distances to be aimed for in factories, offices, and shops.

So, although not of concern to the owners and occupiers of places of work, the guide to the 1971 Act made it abundantly clear that those who were responsible for issuing fire certificates under the Act had, implicitly, to make an assessment of the risk from fire.

While this Act remained in force, and even after the introduction of the Fire Precautions (Workplace) (Amendment) Regulations 1999, those responsible for designated premises still had to apply for a fire certificate as well as carry out and record a fire risk assessment of their buildings.

## The European Council Directives

What brought fire risk assessment to the fore was the adoption in 1989 by the European Community's Council of Ministers of two European Council Directives.

The first, which was adopted in June 1989, is known as the Framework Directive and the second, which was adopted in November 1989, is known as the Workplace Directive. The Framework Directive introduced measures to encourage improvements in the health and safety of workers at work, and the Workplace Directive prescribed minimum health and safety requirements with which all workplaces should comply.

Both Directives firmly placed the primary responsibility for ensuring health and safety in the workplace upon the *employer*, and the Framework Directive requires the employer to be in possession of an *assessment of the risks* – including the risks from fire – to health and safety at work.

## The Fire Precautions (Workplace) Regulations 1997

Most of the provisions of these two Directives were incorporated into two sets of Regulations, the Management of Health and Safety at Work Regulations 1992 and the Workplace (Health, Safety and Welfare) Regulations 1992. The first of these sets of Regulations required employers to make an assessment of the risk to the health and safety of those in their employ, and of those whose health or safety could be affected by the activities of the employer's business.

However, Her Majesty's government decided to implement those provisions of the Directives that deal with general fire safety matters by making a new set of Regulations under the Fire Precautions Act 1971.

These Regulations, called the Fire Precautions (Workplace) Regulations 1997, came into force on 1 December 1997 and were amended in 1999. The requirement to carry out a fire risk assessment was central to these Regulations in that, as is made clear in the Home Office/Health and Safety Executive guidance document, *Fire safety – an employer's guide*, the fire precautions that are needed in the workplace are dictated by the level of the fire risk. The declared purpose of the guidance document was to summarise the requirements of the Regulations and to offer advice as to how the requirements may be met.

## Provisions of the Fire Precautions (Workplace) Regulations 1997 as amended by the Fire Precautions (Workplace) (Amendment) Regulations 1999

As a result of the amendments made in 1999 most workplaces were made subject to the legal requirements of the Regulations. These applied to workplaces where persons were employed to work, but did not apply in workplaces that were:

- private dwellings;
- used only by the self-employed;
- constructions sites;
- means of transport;
- mineshafts;
- ships within the meaning of the Merchant Shipping Act (not those permanently moored, under construction or repair, etc.);
- offshore installations or open farm/forestry land.

The Regulations placed the responsibility for maintaining a fire safe workplace on the 'employer'. The principal requirements were as follows:

- to carry out a fire risk assessment of the workplace. All employees and other people who may be affected by a fire in the workplace, including those with special needs who use or may be present at the premises, had to be considered in the assessment;
- if five or more people were employed, the findings of the risk assessment should have been recorded;
- to provide and maintain adequate fire precautions and safeguard those who use the workplace;
- to provide information, instruction and training to employees about the fire precautions in the workplace.

There were six further principal legal duties:

- to nominate people (the employer may nominate themselves in this respect), to undertake any special roles identified in the emergency plan;
- to consult employees (or their representative bodies), about the nomination of people to carry out particular fire safety roles and about proposals for improving fire precautions;
- to inform other employers who also have workplaces in the building of any significant risks identified which might affect the safety of their employees, and to cooperate with other such employers about the measures proposed to reduce or control those risks;

- where there was no employer but an individual had control of premises which contained more than one workplace, they were also responsible for ensuring that the requirements of the fire regulations were complied with in those parts over which they had control;

- to establish a suitable means for contacting the emergency services and ensuring that they could be called easily;

- employees were required to co-operate with their employer to ensure the workplace was safe from fire and not to do anything which would place themselves or other people at risk.

Readers will note the significant similarities between the requirements described above and those of the Regulatory Reform (Fire Safety) Order which are described in the next section of this chapter. Another important issue to note is that, as of 1 October 2006, the Workplace Regulations no longer apply and workplaces are from that point subject to the requirements of the new legislation.

## Regulatory Reform

In 2001, the UK Government introduced new legislation in the form of the Regulatory Reform Act, which would allow existing primary legislation to be changed by means of a Statutory Instrument (a Regulatory Reform Order (RRO)) provided that the change would remove or reduce a burdensome feature in the legislation and that, in addition, it neither removes any necessary protection from any person nor prevents any person from continuing to exercise any right of freedom that might reasonably be expected to continue. It is by this route – Regulatory Reform Order – that the reform of fire safety legislation has been achieved.

## Provisions of the Regulatory Reform (Fire Safety) Order 2005

The introduction of the Regulatory Reform (Fire Safety) Order, from 1 October 2006, probably represents the biggest reform of fire safety law in over 30 years. The stated aim of the Fire Safety Order is to simplify, rationalise and consolidate the law with respect to fire safety in buildings in use. For example, it amends more than 50 different items of primary legislation which refer to fire safety, including the Fire Precautions Act, discussed earlier in this chapter, which ceases to have effect. A fire certificate issued under the Fire Precautions Act should not, however, be consigned to the waste bin as it could provide a very useful reference source for the fire risk assessment for the workplace.

It should be noted, however, that that Fire Safety Order applies only in England and Wales. Similar reforms of the fire safety regime in Scotland are to be implemented. The Fire (Scotland) Act 2005 came into force on 2 August 2005.

The new fire safety regime in Scotland is broadly similar to that in England and Wales, is based on fire risk assessment and is applicable to most premises in Scotland but not private dwellings (with the exception of some maintenance requirements in respect of firefighting equipment located in the common areas of private dwellings). Scottish ministers are also given the power to make regulations about the carrying out of fire risk assessments and fire safety in premises covered by the new regime. These are the Fire Safety (Scotland) Regulations 2006. Unlike the Fire Safety Order in England and Wales, the Scottish Regulations place the responsibility for undertaking a fire risk assessment and maintaining fire safety standards, in most instances, upon the 'employer'. It is also anticipated that the Regulations will be complemented by sector specific guidance documents.

A similar reform of fire safety legislation will be implemented in Northern Ireland through the Fire and Rescue Services (Northern Ireland) Order in 2006 which again will have a risk-assessed regime as its focus for the ongoing management of fire safety in workplaces.

The laws implemented in Scotland and Northern Ireland contain requirements based on the European Council directives which underpin the Fire Safety Order and as such will require similar steps to be taken for fire prevention and the management of fire safety in the workplace.

One of the key differences between the Workplace Regulations and the Fire Safety Order is that the latter places a duty upon the 'responsible person' (rather than the employer) to ensure the safety of employees and members of the public that are at their premises. The responsible person has duties under the Fire Safety Order to carry out a risk assessment, implement fire safety measures, and take special measures where there are dangerous substances (Schedule 1 of the Fire Safety Order sets out the matters to be taken into account). The arrangements for enforcement, offences and appeals are also detailed.

The Fire Safety Order is arranged in five parts:

- Part 1 – General.

- Part 2 – Fire safety duties.

- Part 3 – Enforcement.

- Part 4 – Offences and appeals.

- Part 5 – Miscellaneous.

## *Part 1 – General*

This part defines the terms used by the Fire Safety Order, including 'responsible person' and 'general fire precautions', and outlines the duties of the responsible person and where the Fire Safety Order does and does not apply.

The 'responsible person' is defined as meaning 'the employer, if the workplace is to any extent under his control' or, where this does not apply, the occupier as 'the person who has control of the premises' or the owner 'where the person in control of the premises does not have control... of a trade, business or other undertaking'.

'General fire precautions' is defined as meaning the taking of measures:

- to reduce the risk and spread of fire;
- for escape;
- to ensure the escape route can be used at all times;
- to detect fire and warn people of a fire; and
- for training.

Appendix A details areas to which the Regulatory Reform (Fire Safety) Order 2005 does not apply.

## *Part 2 – Fire safety duties*

Part 2 details the duties required of the responsible person. In essence, those duties are to:

- take general fire precautions (see definition above);
- carry out, record, and implement the conclusions of a risk assessment, equipping the premises with appropriate firefighting equipment and with detectors and alarms, and providing suitable emergency routes and exits;
- take special precautions where dangerous substances are present so as to eliminate or reduce the fire risk;
- take particular matters into account when employing young people (set out in Part 2 of Schedule 1) and identify in the risk assessment those people especially at risk;
- ensure that employees, parents of children employed, and others at the premises have relevant fire safety information – including details of dangerous substances at the premises – and that employees have adequate safety training and understand the evacuation procedures;

- nominate a sufficient number of 'competent persons' to assist in implementing preventive and protective measures, including safety drills;
- maintain all fire safety equipment; and
- review the risk assessment when necessary.

### Risk assessment

With respect to the risk assessment, the Fire Safety Order (article 9) states:

'The responsible person must make a suitable and sufficient assessment of the risks to which relevant persons are exposed for the purpose of identifying the general fire precautions he needs to take to comply with the requirements and prohibitions imposed on him by or under this Order.'

The definition of relevant person here is important. The definition given in the Fire Safety Order includes any person who may be lawfully on the premises in addition to any person who may be in the immediate vicinity of the premises who is at risk from a fire on the premises.

The risk assessment must include consideration of matters relating to dangerous substances which are or are liable to be present in or on the premises and take particular account of issues relating to the employment of young persons (anyone under the age of 18).

Recording the risk assessment is also an important part of the process. Article 9(6) requires that as soon as practicable after the assessment is made or reviewed, the responsible person must, in the circumstances described below, record the significant findings of the assessment, including the measures which have been or will be taken by the responsible person and details of any group of persons identified by the assessment as being especially at risk,

- if they employ five or more employees;
- where a licence under enactment is in force in relation to the premises; or
- an alterations notice requiring this is in force in relation to the premises.

### Fire safety arrangements

Similar requirements pertain to the implementation and maintenance of the fire safety arrangements. The Fire Safety Order states (article 11):

'(1) The responsible person must make and give effect to such arrangements as are appropriate, having regard to the size of his undertaking and the nature of its activities, for the effective planning, organisation, control, monitoring and review of the preventive and protective measures.

(2) The responsible person must record the arrangements referred to in paragraph (1) where –

(a) he employs five or more employees;

(b) a licence under an enactment is in force in relation to the premises; or

(c) an alterations notice requiring a record to be made of those arrangements is in force in relation to the premises.'

Preventive and protective measures are defined as those which have been identified in consequence of a risk assessment as the general fire precautions which need to be taken in order to comply with the requirements and prohibitions imposed by or under the Fire Safety Order.

## *Elimination or reduction of risks from dangerous substances*

This regulation requires that:

- where a dangerous substance is present in or on the premises, the risk to relevant persons is either eliminated or reduced so far as is reasonably practicable;

- this must be achieved by replacing a dangerous substance or the use of a dangerous substance with a substance or process which either eliminates or reduces the risk to relevant persons – again so far as is reasonably practicable;

- where it is not reasonably practicable to eliminate the risk the responsible person must apply appropriate measures, consistent with the fire risk assessment, to control the risk and mitigate the detrimental effects of a fire.

The responsible person must:

- arrange for the safe handling, storage and transport of dangerous substances and waste containing dangerous substances; and

- ensure that any conditions necessary pursuant to the Fire Safety Order for eliminating or reducing risk are maintained.

## *Firefighting and fire detection*

The requirements of the Fire Safety Order are that:

- the premises are, to the extent that is appropriate, equipped with appropriate firefighting equipment and with fire detectors and alarms.

In deciding what is appropriate, regard must be given to such matters as the size and use to which the premises is put, the materials used or stored, the equipment it contains, and the maximum number of people likely to be present at any one time. In short, one must have regard to results of the fire risk assessment that will have to be carried out.

As regards firefighting equipment, an appropriate number of suitable extinguishers should be provided, as determined from the results of the fire risk assessment (see Chapter 5 of this book).

In a small premises, the most appropriate fire detector might be the human nose or, moving up the scale, a series of interlinked mains-powered domestic smoke alarms. If the ambient noise levels in a small premises are low, simply shouting 'fire' could be a perfectly acceptable means for giving warning of fire. Alternatively, hand-operated devices such as bells, gongs, or sirens may be used. Such devices should be sited on exit routes where they may be operated safely, and any one such device must be audible throughout the workplace. In larger, or noisier, premises an automatic fire detection and alarm system may be required. With such systems, the break-glass manual call points should be sited next to the exit doors, and the number of bells or sounders should be such that they are clearly audible above the ambient noise level throughout the workplace. As with the means for firefighting, the results of the fire risk assessment should determine the nature and level of sophistication of the fire detection and alarm system.

Any non-automatic firefighting equipment provided – portable fire extinguishers, fire hose reels and fire blankets, for example – should be easily accessible, simple to use and indicated by signs.

The Fire Safety Order (article 13 (3)(c)) states:

• the responsible person shall arrange any necessary contacts with external emergency services, particularly as regards firefighting, rescue work, first aid and emergency medical care.

This reference is to the need to establish, if necessary, contacts with external emergency services. This should not be overlooked; putting out fires is not the only function of local fire brigades. Under section 6 of the Fire and Rescue Services Act 2004 fire authorities are legally obliged to give advice on fire prevention, restricting the spread of fire, and means of escape in case of fire. Every fire authority has a team of fire safety officers who have a wealth of knowledge about all aspects of fire safety and they are there to help.

Article 13 also states:

• the responsible person must, where necessary, take measures for firefighting in the premises, adapted to the nature of the activities carried on there and the size of the undertaking and the premises concerned; and

• the responsible person must, where necessary, also nominate competent persons to implement these measures, and ensure that their number, training, and the equipment available for their use are adequate.

These last two requirements cover factors such as what employees should do on discovering a fire, what to do on hearing the fire alarm – or other signal indicating fire – the selection and use the of the correct extinguisher with which to fight the fire, how to summon the fire brigade, and the evacuation procedure.

In small premises, all these matters could be addressed by the combination of the information displayed on the firefighting equipment and a suitably sited fire action notice.

In large premises, it may be necessary to draw up a properly structured emergency plan, and appoint a suitable number of fire marshals or fire wardens who will be responsible for implementing the plan in the event of fire. The reference to 'competent person' above is defined in the Fire Safety Order as someone with 'sufficient training and experience or knowledge and other qualities'. Hence the training of such people is clearly of crucial importance and is dealt with separately in Chapters 6 and 7 of this book.

*Emergency routes and exits*

Article 14 requires that:

- the number, distribution, and dimensions of emergency routes and exits must be adequate, having regard to the use to which the workplace is put, the equipment it contains, its dimensions, and the maximum number of people likely to be present at any one time;

- in the event of danger, it must be possible for persons to evacuate the premises as quickly and as safely as possible.

As with the appropriateness of the firefighting equipment, the adequacy of emergency routes and exits will largely be determined by the results of the fire risk assessment.

In a modern workplace, it is likely that its construction conforms to the requirements of the Building Regulations and its means of escape may therefore be assumed to be satisfactory. Similarly, if, in the course of a recent inspection by the fire service, the means of escape were found to be satisfactory, then nothing further need be done.

If neither of the above criteria are applicable, or there is uncertainty, there are a number of guidelines to help you to decide upon the adequacy or otherwise of the means of escape:

- in the event of a fire, everyone present must be able to reach a place of safety as quickly and as safely as possible;

- routes and exits must lead as directly as possible to a place of safety;

- the number, distribution and dimensions of emergency routes and exits must be adequate with regard to:
  - ◇ the use of the premises,
  - ◇ the maximum number of people who may be present,
  - ◇ the dimensions of the emergency routes and exits,
  - ◇ the fire hazards that are present;
- emergency doors must open in the direction of travel;
- sliding or revolving doors must not be used for exits specifically intended as emergency exits;
- emergency doors must not be so locked or fastened that they cannot be easily and immediately opened by anyone who requires to use them in an emergency;
- emergency routes and exits must be indicated by signs;
- emergency routes and exits that require illumination must be provided with emergency lighting of adequate intensity in the event that the normal lighting fails.

Although it is not stated in the Fire Safety Order, it is implicit that routes to emergency exits, and the doorways themselves, must be kept clear at all times.

## Procedures for serious and imminent danger and for danger areas

This regulation requires that the responsible person must:

- establish and give effect to appropriate procedures, including safety drills to be followed in the event of serious or imminent danger to relevant persons;
- nominate a sufficient number of competent persons to implement those procedures;
- ensure that no relevant person has access to any area to which it is necessary to restrict access on the grounds of safety unless they have received adequate safety instruction.

Additionally persons must be informed of the nature of any hazards which may cause serious or imminent danger and of the steps taken or to be taken to protect them from it. In the event that a person is exposed to serious or imminent danger they must be enabled to stop work and immediately proceed to a place of safety and should be prevented from resuming work in any situation where there is still a serious and imminent danger.

*Additional emergency measures in respect of dangerous substances*

The responsible person must take additional emergency measures where there are dangerous substances (article 16) to ensure that:

'(a) information on emergency arrangements is available, including –

    (i)   details of relevant work hazards and hazard identification arrangements; and

    (ii)  specific hazards likely to arise at the time of an accident, incident or emergency;

(b) suitable warning and other communication systems are established to enable an appropriate response, including remedial actions and rescue operation, to be made immediately when such an event occurs;

(c) where necessary, before any explosion conditions are reached, visual or audible warnings are given and relevant persons withdrawn; and

(d) where the risk assessment indicates it is necessary, escape facilities are provided and maintained to ensure that, in the event of danger, relevant persons can leave endangered places promptly and safely.'

*Maintenance*

There is a requirement to carry out maintenance. The Fire Safety Order states (article 17 (1)): 'Where necessary in order to safeguard the safety of relevant persons the responsible person must ensure that the premises and any facilities, equipment and devices provided in respect of the premises under this Order... are subject to a suitable system of maintenance and are in an efficient state, in efficient working order and in good repair.'

*Safety assistance*

With few exceptions, there is a requirement for the responsible person to appoint one or more 'competent persons', who shall have sufficient training and experience or knowledge and other qualities to assist the responsible person in undertaking the preventive and protective measures. The Fire Safety Order (article 18 (3)) states: 'The responsible person must ensure that the number of persons appointed [as competent persons], the time available for them to fulfil their functions and the means at their disposal are adequate having regard to the size of the premises, the risks to which relevant persons are exposed and the distribution of those risks throughout the premises.' Preference should be given to employees over non-employees when appointing a competent person.

It is likely that a safety assistant will perform the role of fire safety manager for the premises and have day-to-day responsibility for managing, overseeing and supervising all aspects of the premises' fire safety arrangements.

## Provision of information to employees

There is a general duty within the Fire Safety Order on the responsible person to ensure that all employees are provided with comprehensible and relevant information on the risks identified in the risk assessment; details of preventive and protective measures and the procedures to be undertaken in the event of serious or imminent danger; the identities of those members of staff nominated to undertake specific roles in the event of an emergency; and also any other risks which may exist in other parts of the premises or may be present due to the shared occupancy of premises with others.

Where dangerous substances are present in or on the premises the responsible person must also provide employees with details of the substance, including its name and the associated risk, access to any relevant data sheet, legislative provisions which may apply and the significant findings of the fire risk assessment.

Similar duties are imposed on the responsible person in the case where a child is to be employed. In this event, the information must be provided to the child's parents.

## Provision of information to employers and the self employed from outside undertakings

Article 19 requires the responsible person to ensure that the employer of any employees from an outside undertaking who are working on the premises are provided with relevant information on the risks to those employees and the preventive and protective measures implemented. Employers of others from outside undertakings and their employees working on the premises should also be able to identify anyone nominated by the responsible person to undertake specific duties, including the implementation of evacuation procedures.

## Training

Training of employees is a requirement in the Fire Safety Order (article 21), which states:

'The responsible person must ensure that his employees are provided with adequate safety training –

(a) at the time when they are first employed; and

(b) on their being exposed to new or increased risks because of –

    (i)   their being transferred or given a change of responsibilities within the responsible person's undertaking;

    (ii)  the introduction of new work equipment into, or a change respecting work equipment already in use within, the responsible person's undertaking;

    (iii) the introduction of new technology into the responsible person's undertaking; or

    (iv) the introduction of a new system of work into, or a change respecting a system of work already in use within, the responsible person's undertaking.'

Training must include suitable and sufficient instruction on the appropriate precautions and actions to be taken by employees to safeguard themselves and others on the premises, be provided in a manner appropriate to the risk identified by the risk assessment, be repeated periodically where appropriate, adapted when circumstances change, and carried out in working hours.

## Cooperation and coordination

Where premises are shared with others (including the self employed or those in partnership) each responsible person is required to cooperate and coordinate the findings of their separate fire risk assessments to ensure that any actions taken to ensure the fire safety of the premises are effective throughout. This should include, for example, ensuring that plans for the emergency evacuation of the premises are coordinated alongside arrangements for contact with emergency services.

## General duties of employees

In addition to the responsibilities placed upon the 'responsible person' the Fire Safety Order also places a series of general duties upon all employees (article 23). While at work employees must:

- take reasonable care for the safety of themselves and of other relevant persons;

- cooperate with their employer; and

- inform their employer and others with responsibility for safety of any work situation which represents a serious and immediate danger to safety and any other matter which may be seen as a shortcoming in the employer's fire safety arrangements.

## Part 3 – Enforcement

This part of the Order details who will act as the enforcing authority, the powers of inspectors, and the types of notices that can be served.

It is expected that the responsible person will exercise their duty in implementing and maintaining the required standards, the fire and rescue authority will inspect premises and undertake audits of fire risk assessments to enforce the requirements of the Fire Safety Order but this will be done on a risk-based regime that assumes compliance. All inspection work will be undertaken by the fire and rescue services in accordance with the principles of good enforcement laid down in the government's enforcement concordat.

The fire and rescue authority will continue to target its resources at the premises that are deemed to present the greatest risk to people and the community. This means that premises that present a 'high risk' because they are poorly constructed, poorly managed or have poor fire prevention and protection measures, or just because they have an inherent high risk – such as a basement night club – are likely to be visited more often than premises that are seen as 'low risk' because they are well constructed, well managed and have adequate fire prevention measures.

### Enforcing authority

Enforcement will be by the local fire and rescue authority. However, there are a number of notable exceptions as follows:

- in relation to premises licensed under the Nuclear Installations Act, ships (forming part of HM Navy) undergoing work, and construction sites, the Heath and Safety Executive will be the enforcing authority;

- in armed forces premises enforcement will be the responsibility of the fire service maintained by the Secretary of State for Defence;

- in sports grounds, including stands, enforcement responsibilities lie with the relevant local authority;

- in Crown or United Kingdom Atomic Energy Authority premises a fire inspector or anyone else authorised by the Secretary of State will be responsible for enforcement.

### Powers of inspectors

For the purposes of inspection, an enforcing authority's inspector may:

- enter any premises;

- make any enquiry relating to complying with the Fire Safety Order or the identity of the responsible person;

- require the production of information;

- require any person with responsibility for a premises to provide assistance;

- take samples of articles and substances (for the purpse of ascertaining their fire resistance or flammability); and

- dismantle an article or subject a substance to a process or test.

## Alterations notices

If, in the opinion of the enforcing authority, the premises 'constitute a serious risk to relevant persons… or… may constitute such a risk if a change is made to them or the use to which they are put' an alterations notice may be served (article 29 (1)). Before the responsible person makes any changes in response to the alterations notice, he must notify the enforcing authority of the proposed changes. The alterations notice may, in addition, make other requirements of the responsible person – for example, that he carries out and records the findings of a risk assessment.

## Enforcement notices

The Fire Safety Order (article 30 (1)) states: 'If the enforcing authority is of the opinion that the responsible person or any other person [who has control over the premises] has failed to comply with any provision of this Order or any regulations made under it, the authority may… serve on that person… an enforcement notice.' The enforcement notice may include directions as to the measures necessary to remedy the failure. The enforcing authority may withdraw the notice before the period specified in the notice, and – if an appeal is not pending – may extend the period specified in the notice.

## Prohibition notices

The Fire Safety Order (article 31 (1)) states: 'If the enforcing authority is of the opinion that the use of the premises involves or will involve a risk to relevant persons so serious that use of the premises ought to be prohibited or restricted, the authority may serve on the responsible person or any other person [who has control over the premises]… a prohibition notice.' If the enforcing authority takes the view that the risk is sufficiently serious, the prohibition notice may have immediate effect. As with the enforcement notice, the prohibition notice may include remedial directions.

## Part 4 – Offences and appeals

This part identifies the offences that may be committed under the Fire Safety Order by the responsible person (or any person who has control over the premises) or any other person, the level of punishment on conviction, reasonable defence for a charged person, the appeals procedure, and the powers of the Secretary of State to determine disputes.

### Offences

The Fire Safety Order (article 32) outlines in detail acts or omissions which may be deemed as an offence under the Order.

These principally relate to failures by the responsible person or any other person who has control over the workplace to comply with the requirements of any notice in effect. Similarly, other offences are outlined which apply to any person and relate in general to failures to comply with the requirements of the Regulations, false reporting, obstructing or deceiving an inspector and, again, failing to comply with the requirements of a notice in force.

### Conviction

Punishments on conviction range from a fine to imprisonment depending on the offence. Where an offence is shown to have been committed by a 'body corporate', any director, manager, secretary, or other officer of the company may also be found guilty of an offence if consent, connivance, or neglect can be proved.

### Defence

The Fire Safety Order (article 33) states: '… it is a defence for the person charged to prove that he took all reasonable precautions and exercised all due diligence to avoid the commission of such an offence.' It is also stated (article 34): '… it is for the accused to prove that it was not practicable or reasonably practical to do more than was in fact done to satisfy the duty or requirement.'

### Appeals

A person served with an alterations notice, enforcement notice, or a prohibition notice may appeal to a magistrates' court within 21 days from the day on which it was served. The court has the right to modify the notice if it rejects the appeal. Where an appeal is brought against an alterations notice or enforcement notice, it has the effect of suspending operation of the notice; when appealing a prohibition notice, the notice is only suspended if the court so directs. If the verdict of the magistrates' court is not satisfactory to either side, a further appeal may be made to the Crown Court.

*Disputes*

When a responsible person or other person who has control over the premises and the enforcing authority cannot agree on the measures necessary to remedy a failure, the matter may be referred to the Secretary of State, whose decision will be binding on both parties.

### Part 5 – Miscellaneous

This part details:

- the requirements for firefighters' switches for luminous tube signs and maintenance of facilities, equipment, and devices for the protection of firefighters;

- the duty on employers not to charge employees for anything required by the Fire Safety Order;

- special provisions for licensed premises;

- areas of overlap with byelaws and the Health and Safety at Work etc Act 1974;

- the duty to consult the enforcing authority before passing plans;

- the duty upon government departments and authorities intending to take action that will or may result in changes to any measure required by the Fire Safety Order;

- requirements for the serving of notices;

- application of the Fire Safety Order to the Crown and Houses of the Parliament;

- the onus on the Secretary of State to provide guidance to assist responsible persons;

- application to visiting forces, etc;

- subordinate provisions; and

- repeals, revocations, amendments, and transitional provisions.

## Other legislation, premises affected and means of compliance

The Fire Safety Order will also embrace premises covered by other legislation, such as the Licensing Act 2003, regardless of whether the license is for alcohol or entertainment. The difference will be that the fire and rescue authority will be the enforcing authority for general fire precautions within licensed and registered premises. No licensing or registration authority will be able to impose conditions on premises that relate to general fire precautions.

The Licensing Act 2003 introduces a requirement for applicants to serve applications for licenses to sell or supply alcohol, provide regulated entertainment or provide late night refreshment directly upon the fire and rescue authority. On receipt of an application, the fire and rescue authority may make a representation against the grant of a license or take independent enforcement action in order to address inadequate proposals regarding the provision and/or management of fire precautions.

There is a myriad of small businesses where fewer than five people are employed and, although a fire risk assessment should be undertaken for these workplaces, there is no obligation to record it (unless, as described above, a licence or an alterations notice requiring this is in force). It would be good practice, however, to keep an elementary form of written assessment, as both a reminder of the risks that have been identified and also to show the fire brigade that an assessment has been undertaken should they make a goodwill visit to the premises. Provision could be made on the document to allow it to be amended, initialled and dated periodically to indicate that it has been reviewed.

There are also some workplaces – such as small care homes with few staff, or sheltered accommodation with a warden on site – where there is potentially a significant risk to life. In these cases good management practice would again indicate that the fire risk assessment should be recorded even though there is no duty to do so in the Fire Safety Order.

Whatever the nature of the business and whatever size the company may be, if a building is shared with other organisations these employers must be informed of any significant risks, found during the fire risk assessment, that may have a bearing on the safety of their employees. Close liaison should be maintained with the fire safety managers of the other organisations to allow co-operation to eliminate, reduce or control the risk of fire in the premises.

# Fire risk assessment methods

In the nuclear, chemical, and petrochemical industries, assessing the risks peculiar to these fields of activity can entail the use of quite sophisticated mathematical techniques, and such assessments must be done by expertly trained people.

The fire risk assessment that will be required in other types of occupancy is very definitely not in this league. In the vast majority of cases, it will be a relatively straightforward and simple task that may be carried out by the company fire safety manager.

When approaching the task there are only three 'rules' that should be borne in mind:

- there is no single correct way in which the assessment should be made; there are no national or international standards relating to fire risk assessment. Put another way, the first rule of risk assessment is that there are no rules!

- the methodology to be adopted should be a practical, structured and, above all, common-sense one.

- while the legal responsibility for carrying out the assessment rests with the employer, in complex workplaces he is at liberty to seek the help of his own experts or, if necessary, the help of outside consultants.

Because, in larger workplaces, different areas may represent quite different levels of risk, it will, in such cases, be more appropriate to undertake individual risk assessments for each of these areas rather than just one risk assessment for the whole of the workplace.

This chapter describes four possible methods, which are in no way to be taken as definitive examples of the techniques that they employ:

- the five-step method suggested in guidance given to the Fire Precautions (Workplace) Regulations 1997 (as amended 1999) in the publication *Fire Safety. An employer's guide* and subsequently recommended in guidance in support of the Regulatory Reform (Fire Safety) Order 2005 in the Government guides entitled *Fire safety risk assessment*;

- the risk factor matrix method;

- an industrial method;
- an algorithmic method;
- a 'traffic light' system.

## The five-step method

This method entails a two-fold process:

- identifying the fire hazards, that is to say the readily combustible or highly flammable materials, sources of heat, and unsatisfactory structural features;
- assessing the fire risk, which is the likelihood that a fire will occur and the consequences of such a fire on the staff in the workplace.

The overall process may be carried out in five steps:

- *Step 1:* identify the fire hazards.
- *Step 2:* identify the people at risk.
- *Step 3:* evaluate, remove, reduce and protect from risks.
- *Step 4:* record, plan, instruct, inform and train.
- *Step 5:* review.

### *Step 1*

Identifying hazards entails noting readily combustible materials or highly flammable substances. These would include such things as paints and thinners, flammable solvents, solvent-based adhesives, flammable gases, combustible plastic foams, large areas of bare hardboard, highly flammable and/or reactive chemicals or any other sources of fuel.

It also entails noting sources of heat such as flames or sparks from processes, sources of frictional heat, ovens, incinerators, oil or gas-fired equipment or heaters, matches and lighters, ducts or flues, lightbulbs close to combustible materials, electrical leads, any electrical equipment, faulty wiring, portable heaters and any other sources of ignition.

Structural features that would constitute hazards and should therefore be identified would include such things as ducts and flues, unstopped holes that have been cut into fire walls for the provision of services such as cables and pipework, large areas of hardboard, chipboard, or blockboard, uncompartmented roof spaces, excessively long escape routes and so on.

## Step 2

In identifying people who could be at risk in a fire one would have in mind any who may be asleep in the workplace, those present in large numbers, those who are unfamiliar with the layout of the workplace and/or the exit routes, those who may be exposed to a particular or specific fire risk, and those who have impaired sight, hearing or mobility.

One would also note any people who would be unable to react quickly enough or are unaware of the danger of fire because they work in remote areas, because they have learning difficulties or because they are outside contractors who are unaware of fire risks.

## Step 3

On completion of Step 2 sufficient information will have been gathered to allow for a sensible evaluation to be made of the risk of a fire occurring and the risks to people from fire. This will lead to decisions being made as to the removal or reduction of such risks. The removal or reduction of hazards entailed in this stage of the risk assessment can have enormous benefits insofar as, at the end of the process, a much safer working environment will have been produced. For each of the hazards that have been identified in Step 1, consider whether it could be removed, reduced, replaced, separated, protected, repaired or cleaned.

One could, for example, remove excessive amounts of combustible materials, reduce the area of combustible wall linings, replace tungsten filament bulbs with fluorescent fittings and solvent-based adhesives with water-based pastes, separate sources of heat from combustible materials, protect electrical equipment with thermostats, residual current devices and correctly rated fuses, repair torn upholstered furniture, clean dirty flues and ducts.

It should also be decided at this stage whether any of these removals or reductions are to be undertaken immediately, in the medium term, or in the long term.

In addition to taking the above preventative measures, consideration should also be given to protective measures. Decisions need to be made regarding the adequacy of fire safety measures and whether any improvements are necessary. Possible improvements would include such steps as:

*   the reduction of evacuation times/escape route lengths;
*   the provision of additional escape routes;
*   the installation of more fire alarm call points;
*   the provision of more fire signs;

- the installation of a sprinkler system;
- the institution of better programmes of fire safety training;
- the appointment of fire wardens.

## Step 4

In most circumstances (see Chapter 1 for more details) it will be necessary to record the significant findings of the risk assessment. This should include the significant hazards found to be present, the details of any persons who may be a particular risk, the steps taken or equipment/facilities provided to minimise or otherwise mitigate the hazards identified and any further actions needed.

The recording of these findings will assist in the development of an emergency plan for the premises, which will explain to staff and others the actions to take in the event of a fire. One must ensure that there is adequate liaison, cooperation and coordination with others who may have responsibilities for fire safety matters in or on other parts of the premises – it is unlikely that any emergency plan will work without this. In addition to the development of the plan, it is important also to provide suitable instruction to staff and others who may be on the premises, such as contractors, on how to prevent fires and the actions to take upon hearing the alarm or discovering a fire. The significant findings of the fire risk assessment and the emergency plan should also be used to help develop suitable induction training for new members of staff which should be provided as soon as possible after they are appointed.

The type and duration of training provided for staff will be dependent on the size and nature of the premises. However, it is important to ensure that all staff are aware of the actions to take in the event of a fire, the location and, when appropriate, the use of firefighting equipment, the location of escape routes, significant hazards and the importance of maintaining good standards of fire safety including good housekeeping practices.

## Step 5

Keeping the assessment under review is one of the most important aspects – and often forgotten. If for any reason it is believed that the fire risk assessment is no longer valid it will be necessary to undertake a review and consider the impacts this may have on the emergency plan and staff training. There are any number of circumstances which may trigger the need for a review including when:

- material alterations are made to the structure or layout of the premises;
- there is a change to a process, pattern of storage or similar function in the workplace;

- there is a change in the use of an area of the premises;

- a hazardous material is to be introduced to the premises or there is a change to the quantity or nature of a hazardous material that is already present;

- there are significant changes to the number or location of staff, visitors or other persons expected to be present (particularly if people sleep on the premises);

- there is a significant change in the mobility level or other factors influencing the response of anyone present in the event of an emergency;

- there are changes to the management of the premises.

A sensible approach would be to consider the impact of any planned changes before implementing them. In any case, it will be necessary to keep the assessment under periodic review to ensure that precautions continue to work effectively.

## The risk factor matrix method ·

Unlike the five-step method, this method attempts to put the risk assessment onto a semi-quantitative basis. However, it cannot be stressed too strongly that the numbers involved are purely relative, and that they therefore have no absolute significance whatsoever.

While all risks are made up of two elements: the probability that an event will occur and the harmful or unwanted consequences of that occurrence, the relative contributions that these two elements make to the risk may vary considerably.

To give an everyday example of this point, consider two gambling risks, the tossing of a coin to decide the winner of a wager, and the playing of Russian roulette. In each case the unwanted or harmful consequence is losing the gamble. In the first case the probability of losing is 1 in 2, whereas in the second case it is only 1 in 6, three times less likely. However, the consequences of losing are hugely different; the loss of cash in one case and the loss of one's life in the other.

For the purposes of this method, we define the probability that a fire event will occur as the fire likelihood, and the consequences of that event as the fire hazard.

### Quantifying the fire hazard and the fire likelihood

This is easily done. First we classify the fire hazards by describing them as being between negligible and very severe, and by assigning a numerical value, H, to each description.

Similarly, we may classify the fire likelihood by describing it as being between unlikely to very likely, and by assigning a numerical value, L, to each of these descriptions. A typical classification table is shown in Figure 3.1.

| FIRE HAZARD | | FIRE LIKELIHOOD | |
|---|---|---|---|
| DESCRIPTION | VALUE (H) | DESCRIPTION | VALUE (L) |
| Negligible | 1 | Unlikely | 1 |
| Slight | 2 | Possible | 2 |
| Moderate | 3 | Quite possible | 3 |
| Severe | 4 | Likely | 4 |
| Very severe | 5 | Very likely | 5 |

*Figure 3.1. Assigning numerical values to fire hazards and fire likelihood*

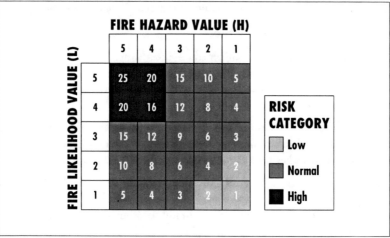

*Figure 3.2. A 5 x 5 risk factor matrix*

In using this method to perform a fire risk assessment, one decides the values of both H and L that best fit the circumstances in the area being assessed. It is important to realise that in using this method we assign values to H and L for the *area as a whole*.

## A formula for the risk factor

Remembering that the two elements of risk are the fire hazard and the fire risk, it would be reasonable to define something that we shall call the risk factor, F, by the simple formula:

$$F = H \times L$$

*Figure 3.3. Fire hazard values versus fire likelihood values*

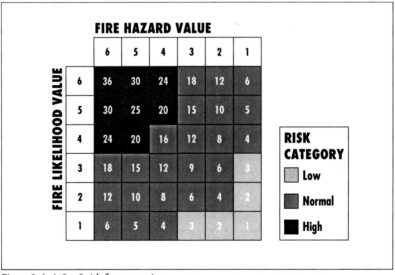

*Figure 3.4. A 6 x 6 risk factor matrix*

If we apply the risk factor formula to all possible combinations of fire hazard values and fire likelihood values we obtain a set of 25 numbers – the risk factors – which could then be displayed as a two-dimensional grid which we could call a risk factor matrix. An example of such a 5 x 5 matrix is shown in Figure 3.2. Alternatively, one could plot fire hazard values against fire likelihood values as is shown in Figure 3.3.

There is no particular reason for having illustrated this method by using a 5 x 5 matrix; it could just as well have been a 6 x 6 matrix, or an unsymmetrical matrix such as, for example, a 7 x 4 matrix. To create a 6 x 6 matrix, all we would need to do is to add the description 'catastrophic' to our fire hazard classification, and add the description of 'almost certain' to our fire likelihood classification; the resulting matrix is shown in Figure 3.4.

The various levels of severity of the fire hazard, negligible, slight etc, could, more specifically, be quantified in terms of the degree of harm to people, the duration of business interruption, the amount of financial loss or the extent of property damage. Examples of how this may be done are shown in Figures 3.5 to 3.8.

The final task in this method is to decide the ranges of the risk factors that will correspond to the three categories of risk. On the assumption that the majority of workplaces would be of normal risk, with very few of low risk, and perhaps slightly more of high risk, one could, for this 5 x 5 matrix, arbitrarily assign low risk to risk factor values of 1-2, normal risk to values of 3-15, and high risk to values of 16-25. The risk factor values assigned to each risk category have to be considered separately for each form of matrix.

| SEVERITY | HARM CAUSED |
|---|---|
| Negligible | Minor bruises/discomfort |
| Slight | Some minor injuries |
| Moderate | Many minor injuries |
| Severe | Some major injuries |
| Very severe | Many major injuries and fewer than five deaths |
| Catastrophic | Five or more deaths |

Figure 3.5. Severity of the fire hazard in terms of harm to people

| SEVERITY | DURATION OF INTERRUPTION |
|---|---|
| Negligible | A few hours |
| Slight | One day |
| Moderate | One week |
| Severe | One month |
| Very severe | Up to six months |
| Catastrophic | Six months to one year |

Figure 3.6. Severity of the fire hazard in terms of business interruption

| SEVERITY | FINANCIAL LOSS |
|----------|----------------|
| Negligible | *£100 or less* |
| Slight | *£101 to £500* |
| Moderate | *£501 to £1000* |
| Severe | *£1001 to £500 000* |
| Very severe | *£500 001 to £1 000 000* |
| Catastrophic | *Multi £1 000 000* |

*Figure 3.7. Severity of the fire hazard in terms of financial loss*

| SEVERITY | DAMAGE/LOSS |
|----------|-------------|
| Negligible | *Slight smoke damage* |
| Slight | *Loss/damage to some equipment* |
| Moderate | *Loss of one floor of building* |
| Severe | *Whole building damaged* |
| Very severe | *Total loss of whole building* |
| Catastrophic | *Loss of whole site* |

*Figure 3.8. Severity of the fire hazard in terms of damage to or loss of property*

## An industrial method

This is in essence a variant of the risk factor matrix method, although the terminology is slightly different. Our classification table is drawn up in terms of the frequency of occurrence of an unwanted fire-related event or situation – in general we could call these 'defects in fire safety' – and the harm that fire-related event or situation would cause were it to occur. The magnitudes of these two elements of the risk are indicated by giving each of them a numerical value – X for the frequency and Y for the harm.

An example of such a classification table is shown in Figure 3.9.

| FREQUENCY | VALUE (X) | HARM | VALUE (Y) |
|-----------|-----------|------|-----------|
| Uncommon | 1 | Trivial injury | 1 |
| Infrequent | 2 | Minor injury | 2 |
| Occasional | 3 | One major injury | 3 |
| Frequent | 4 | Several major injuries | 4 |
| Regular | 5 | One death | 5 |
| Common | 6 | Multiple deaths | 6 |

*Figure 3.9. An industrial method classification table*

For each defect in fire safety, the risk factor is simply defined as the mathematical product of its X and Y values. That is, the risk factor is defined by:

$$\text{Risk factor} = XY$$

Unlike the risk factor matrix method, where we compute a *single* risk factor for the *whole* area being assessed, here we calculate a risk factor for each of the defects in fire safety found in the area and then calculate the *average* risk factor. This average risk factor is the sum of all the individual risk factors [which in mathematical shorthand is written $\sum(XY)$] divided by their number, n. The average risk factor can therefore be written as $\sum(XY)/n$

This average risk factor is then expressed as a percentage of the *maximum risk factor,* and this percentage figure is called the risk rating for the area.

Clearly, for the 6 x 6 classification table that we have used, the maximum value of the risk factor will be 36 (6 x 6) and therefore a risk factor of 1 would be

$$100 \times \frac{1}{36} = 2.8\%$$

of the maximum risk factor. (For a 5 x 5 matrix, the maximum value of the risk factor is 25 (5 x 5) and a risk factor of 1 would be 100 x 1/25 = 4% of the maximum risk factor.)

Therefore, for our 6 x 6 classification, the risk rating is defined by the equation:

$$\text{Risk rating} = 2.8 \times \sum(XY)/n$$

The final step in this method is to decide upon ranges of values for the risk rating that would indicate that the area being assessed should be assigned a risk category of low, normal, or high. *Possible* ranges are those shown in Figure 3.10.

As a generalised example of this method in use, consider a workplace comprising two buildings, A and B. In undertaking the fire risk assessment, building A was found to contain five defects in fire safety, and building B contained four. Each of these defects was assigned X and Y values as shown in Figure 3.11. Also shown in Figure 3.11 is the sum of the risk factors, the average risk factor, and the risk rating for each of the two buildings in the workplace.

| RISK RATING | RISK CATEGORY |
|---|---|
| Less than 15% | Low |
| 15% to 50% | Normal |
| Greater than 50% | High |

*Figure 3.10. Risk categories corresponding to calculated risk ratings*

| BUILDING A X x Y | BUILDING B X x Y |
|---|---|
| 6 x 5 = 30 | 2 x 2 = 4 |
| 5 x 6 = 30 | 3 x 3 = 9 |
| 5 x 5 = 25 | 2 x 3 = 6 |
| 6 x 5 = 30 | 1 x 2 = 2 |
| 4 x 5 = 20 | |
| Total (XY) = 135 | Total (XY) = 21 |
| Average (XY) = 135/5 = 27 | Average (XY) = 21 / 4 = 5.25 |
| Risk rating = 27 x 2.8 = 75.6% | Risk rating = 5.25 x 2.8 = 14.7% |

*Figure 3.11 An example of a fire risk assessment using the industrial method*

Using the data in Figure 3.10, building A is of high fire risk category and building B is (just) of low fire risk category.

When considering the harm resulting from a defect in fire safety, note should be taken of the value of any fire protection equipment installed. A sprinkler system, for example, may have the effect of reducing major injuries to trivial injuries.

## An algorithmic method

An algorithm is a two-dimensional diagrammatic representation of the steps to be undertaken in order to make a decision, solve a problem or carry out a process. In short, it is a flowchart.

An example of the type of fire risk assessment algorithm that might be used is shown in Figure 3.12. It must however be stressed that this algorithm is in no way to be taken as the perfect, definitive, example of this method; it is merely one of many similar algorithms that could be used.

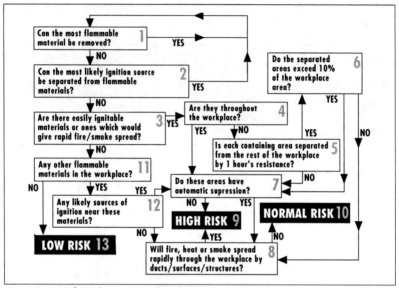

*Figure 3.12. A fire risk assessment algorithm*

## How to use the algorithm

Starting with box 1, one first identifies the most flammable or combustible material in the area and then asks the question 'can it be removed or its amount reduced?' If the answer is 'yes', it should be removed from the area or its amount should be reduced. Of the flammable or combustible materials that remain, one again identifies the most flammable or combustible and then again asks the question 'can it be removed or its amount reduced ?' If the answer is 'yes' it should be removed from the area or its amount should be reduced. This process is repeated until the answer to the question in box 1 is 'no', at which stage the amount of flammable or combustible materials in the area has been reduced to what is considered to be an irreducible minimum.

Moving on to box 2, one first identifies the most likely source of ignition and then asks the question 'can it be separated from flammable or combustible materials?' If the answer is 'yes', the separation is effected and, of the sources of ignition that remain, one identifies the one considered to be the most likely source of ignition and again asks the question 'can it be separated from flammable or combustible materials?' If the answer is 'yes', the separation is effected. This process of identifying sources of ignition and separating them from things that will burn is continued until the answer to the question in box 2 is 'no', at which stage no further separations can be effected.

It is perhaps worth noting that having gone as far as one can by way of removing and/or reducing materials that will burn, and of separating those that remain from sources of ignition, one has, by using the algorithm, reached virtually the same point in the assessment as is reached when one has completed Step 1 of the five-step method. None of the questions in the algorithm in Figure 3.12 identify people at risk, which is Step 2 in the five-step method. The 'people factor' would have to be addressed separately, either by means of a separate algorithm or by an alternative method.

Apart from these first two steps, which constitute cyclical loops, all the other steps in the algorithm form a self-explanatory linear progression which will lead to the conclusion that the workplace is to be categorised as being of high, normal, or low risk. If, for example, the answers to the questions in boxes 3 and 11 were both 'no', then the area being assessed would fall into the low fire risk category.

However, suppose that the answers to the questions in boxes 3 and 4 had been 'yes', and that the answer to the question in box 7 had been 'no'. This would mean that one would have, throughout an area that was not protected by an automatic suppression system – such as an automatic sprinkler installation – materials that would give rise to the rapid spread of fire, heat, or smoke. Such a situation would mean that the area in question would be classified as being in the high fire risk category.

The installation of an automatic sprinkler system would change to 'yes' the answer to the question in box 7, and if this were to be followed by a 'no' answer to the question in box 8, then what had been classified as a high fire risk area would now be in the normal fire risk category. At this point in the algorithm one has, in effect, reached the same point in the assessment as when Step 3 of the five-step method has been completed.

Even with this rather brief account of how one may use such an algorithm, it should be clear that this method is not all that dissimilar to the initial principal processes which form the five-step method. Remember that Steps 4 and 5 dealt mainly with recording the assessment, developing an emergency plan and keeping the assessment under review.

## A 'traffic light' system

The fire risk in premises can also be assessed and audited by the degree of observation of a 'traffic light' system. This involves assessing degrees of compliance of the various elements of the fire safety management of the premises to various codes of practice and giving them percentage markings interpreted by a colour coding system.

An example could be as follows:

1. *Gold or a corporate colour:* compliance with the company fire safety standards, British or other relevant standards, recognised good practice and fire safety legislation.

2. *Green:* compliance with British or other relevant standards, recognised good practice and fire safety legislation.

3. *Amber:* compliance with recognised good practice and fire safety legislation.

4. *Red:* a lesser standard of fire safety.

Each aspect of fire safety provisions would be rated separately with a percentage score being assigned for each and the significant findings would include a list of remedial actions that should be undertaken to improve matters.

## The benefits of fire risk assessment

Any of the four methods described in this chapter may be used to undertake a fire risk assessment. None of them is the definitive method and even those which appear to be quantitative are, at best, only semi-quantitative in nature. However, a carefully carried out fire risk assessment will produce three distinct benefits for the owner or occupier of the workplace.

First, there will be compliance with the statutory requirement to make an assessment of the risk to people in the event of fire. Secondly, and more importantly, the workplace will, by virtue of the hazard reduction part of the exercise, have been made a much safer place in which to work. Thirdly, a realistic assessment of the risk from fire must mean that what are no doubt scarce financial resources are devoted to necessary fire safety measures; in short, it will lead to a more cost-effective use of the fire safety manager's budget.

# Identifying fire hazards in the workplace

There are three requirements for a fire to occur. There must be a source of ignition, something to burn and air to assist the combustion process. The first two of these we can identify and control in our places of work but as air is all around us wherever we are it is only in special circumstances that restrictions on the presence of air or oxygen are considered when undertaking a risk assessment. In this chapter a detailed description is given of a fire risk assessment that is based on the five-step method outlined in Chapter 3.

The first principle of a fire risk assessment is to identify sources of ignition and combustible materials, reduce their levels of occurrence in the workplace and ensure that they are kept apart as far as is practicable.

Having minimised the likelihood of a fire occurring, there will still be a chance, albeit a lesser one, of a fire and so the effect of a fire on people who are present must also be considered. This will lead to consideration being given to the fire protection equipment installed, the fire safety management procedures, the nature of the building concerned, and the equipment or process machinery that is in use, in order to determine whether any fire safety improvements are called for.

The assessment should take into account:

*   the type of work being undertaken;

*   the materials being used or stored;

*   the contents of the workplace, including equipment, furniture and furnishings;

*   the form of construction of the workplace, including the internal linings;

*   the size and layout of the workplace;

*   the number of people who are likely to be present, whether staff or visitors, and their ability to respond to an emergency.

Having completed the assessment, the findings should be recorded and an emergency plan be prepared. Carrying out a fire risk assessment is not a one-off affair, it cannot be undertaken and then forgotten because even over a short period of time patterns of work change, new materials are brought into the workplace and updating working practices may result in the introduction of additional sources of ignition. The number of staff may also change markedly and refurbishment or redecoration may result in escape routes being modified and additional hazards being introduced.

The stages in carrying out a risk assessment are shown in Figure 4.1 and this chapter takes us through each step.

## Stage 1: Identifying the fire hazards

### *1(a) Sources of ignition*

Virtually every workplace contains potential sources of ignition, although if they do not involve naked flames they may not be perceived as such. Some hazards, such as ovens and soldering irons, may be obvious and present a continual threat while others, such as blowlamps being used by contractors, may be transient or only pose a problem in case of malfunction or misuse.

Light bulbs are often overlooked but are almost always present and generally will not pose a hazard if used correctly for the purpose that was intended. If, however, piles of paper in a stationery store are left in contact with a bulb then a fire may result. The same danger exists in the case of fluorescent light tubes where there is an additional danger of the fittings overheating if a fault should occur in the circuitry. A flickering tube may indicate that such a fault exists.

Similarly, most forms of convector heaters are quite safe in normal operation but may cause a fire if covered, for example to dry wet clothing.

The most common sources of heat in the workplace include:

- flames or sparks from a work process such as welding, cutting, grinding or the use of a hot air gun;

- electrical equipment;

- frictional heat;

- electrostatic discharges;

- ovens, kilns, open hearths, furnaces or incinerators;

- boilers, engines and other oil burning equipment;

- matches, lighters, candles and smoking materials;

- open gas flames and gas burning equipment;

- light bulbs and fluorescent tubes if too close to combustible materials;

- electrical extension leads and adapters;

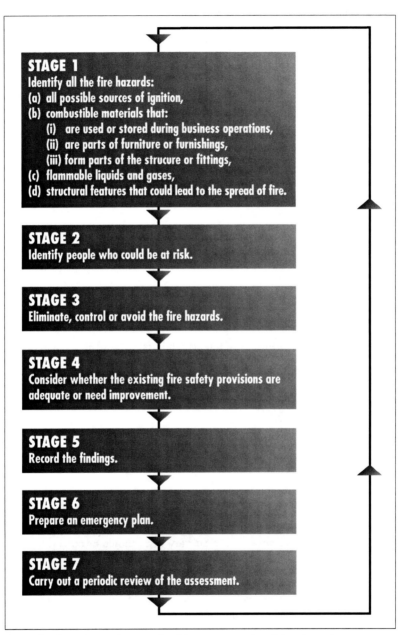

**STAGE 1**
Identify all the fire hazards:
(a) all possible sources of ignition,
(b) combustible materials that:
    (i)   are used or stored during business operations,
    (ii)  are parts of furniture or furnishings,
    (iii) form parts of the strucure or fittings,
(c) flammable liquids and gases,
(d) structural features that could lead to the spread of fire.

**STAGE 2**
Identify people who could be at risk.

**STAGE 3**
Eliminate, control or avoid the fire hazards.

**STAGE 4**
Consider whether the existing fire safety provisions are adequate or need improvement.

**STAGE 5**
Record the findings.

**STAGE 6**
Prepare an emergency plan.

**STAGE 7**
Carry out a periodic review of the assessment.

*Figure 4.1. Stages in carrying out a fire risk assessment and analysing the results*

- faulty or damaged wiring or electrical equipment;

- portable heaters;

- cooking equipment, including deep fat fryers.

The threat of arson should not be overlooked, as it is one of the most common causes of fire both in homes and in the workplace.

The list above is by no means exhaustive and is provided merely as a guide. Appendix B is intended to assist in identifying source of ignition in your workplace and space is provided for adding further sources of ignition which you identify as posing a threat.

## 1(b) Combustible materials

All of the combustible materials in, or forming part of, the premises should be identified and their hazard assessed. Some, such as wallpaper on the walls, should cause little concern, but others, especially those that may be easily ignited, may require action to be taken to eliminate, control or avoid the hazard. Items to be considered include:

### (i) Materials that form part of the business operations

- large quantities of paper, including files, folders and contents of waste bins;

- many plastics materials, especially foamed plastics;

- packaging materials;

- fabrics and clothing;

- timber, hardboard, chipboard and similar products;

- chemicals which may be combustible or react with other chemicals to produce heat;

- display and exhibition materials.

Large numbers of video or computer tapes have been found to be a particular hazard and purpose-designed storage for these items should be provided.

### (ii) Furniture and furnishings
All new furniture purchased should comply with the Furniture and Furnishings (Fire) (Safety) Regulations 1988, but, specially in older premises, there may be items still in use which predate this legislation. Other items, such as curtains, are not subject to these Regulations but should also be assessed regularly, together with the furniture, to ensure that they are in good repair, and are still appropriate for the area and the use to which they are put. These items include:

- armchairs;

- upholstered benches and stools;

- beds and bedding where there is sleeping accommodation;

- wardrobes and dressing tables;

- dining chairs and tables;

- curtains, drapes and cushions;

- artificial foliage, trees, shrubs and flowers;

- desks and office furnishings;

- carpets.

Many companies wish to make a good impression on visitors when they first enter the building and are tempted to fit carpets in the reception area and perhaps elsewhere. Some carpets ignite readily and burn to produce large volumes of smoke and toxic gases. They are therefore not suitable for use on escape routes. New floor coverings should comply with BS 5287: *Specification for the assessment and labelling of textile floor coverings tested to BS 4790.* (BS 4790 is the method for determination of the effects of a small source of ignition on textile floor coverings (hot nut method).)

For similar reasons, artificial plants are often used in public and reception areas. There is no British Standard for these and so they should be tested by removing a small piece of each component, taking the samples out of the building and applying a flame. Ignition is acceptable on the application of the flame, but on its removal the flaming should not spread beyond the area first ignited. It is suggested that items which produce flaming droplets are not placed on escape routes. Any foliage which is protected by fire resistant treatment may need to be tested and retreated after washing or cleaning. Dried flowers and grasses should not be sprayed with flammable substances such as hair lacquer as this would increase the likelihood of ignition and rate of fire spread.

### (iii) Parts of the structure and fittings
It is often thought that buildings are constructed of non-combustible materials such as concrete and brick and therefore do not burn. While this may be true of the structure itself, apart from in the case of wooden buildings, there is a wide spectrum of materials that are used in lining and separation that ignite comparatively readily and make a significant contribution to the development of a fire. They may also produce copious quantities of smoke and toxic gases which pose a threat to the occupants. When carrying out a risk assessment, consideration should be given to features such as:

# Case history: Poor management of smoking materials

A fire was discovered in the foyer of a cinema by a member of staff while clearing up after the evening session. The fire brigade was called and the staff evacuated from the building. The fire started in a waste paper bin and subsequently spread up a curtain and entered the ceiling cavity. From here the flames spread to the roof and quickly involved the whole building.

It took four hours for the fire brigade, using two aerial monitors and 12 jets, to bring the fire under control. The fire was so severe that the cinema, a famous landmark in the town, had to be demolished.

Investigators recovered a time lapse security videotape from the debris which condensed one minute into six seconds. Although this did not contain a complete record of the origin of the incident, shortly before the outbreak of fire it showed a full ashtray on the reception desk close to the waste bin. Later, the ashtray was empty but smoke was coming from the bin. It therefore appeared that the ashtray had been emptied into the partly full waste paper bin.

- combustible wall and ceiling linings;

- large notice boards and tapestries;

- composite (sandwich) panels incorporating combustible insulation;

- timber shelving;

- temporary room or office partitions;

- plastic fluorescent-light diffusers;

- unsuitable glazing.

Unsuitable, non-fire-resistant, glazing can lead to fire spread from area to area or, in the immediate vicinity of some external escape routes, can pose a threat to life. Even fire-resistant glazing can, in some instances, radiate sufficient heat to be a potential threat to people attempting to escape. Glazing on or immediately adjacent to escape routes should therefore be assessed – as should glazing in compartment walls – and replaced if necessary.

## 1(c) Flammable liquids and gases

Large volumes of flammable liquids should be stored outside the premises in accordance to the guidelines published by the Health and Safety Executive. Only small volumes, adequate for the period of work, should be kept inside the buildings. Such liquids should be in sealed cans or safety containers where possible. The liquids to be considered are not only those available for the production processes but must include any present for other uses, such as small volumes of petrol for the lawn mower and small amounts of solvents kept for cleaning purposes. When carrying out the assessment consider:

- petroleum products;

- cooking oils;

- motor oils, other lubricants and hydraulic fluids;

- solvents and degreasing agents;

- paints and thinners;

- specialist chemicals used in production processes;

- propane, butane, acetylene and other flammable gases in cylinders.

A note should also be made of aerosol cans, especially if large numbers of these are stored in the building.

# Case history: Design of shop and large number of aerosol cans hamper firefighting

When the fire brigade arrived at a chemist's shop at 0751 hours they found a fire that had been burning intensely for over half an hour. Access to the shop was hampered by the layout of the premises, which was tunnel-shaped, with a large entrance at the front and a small exit at the rear. There were solid walls to the sides and a substantial ceiling which led to the shop becoming extremely hot and smoke logged. The heat was so great that firefighters wearing breathing apparatus were unable to remain in the building for very long.

A further hazard to the firefighters was the nature of the stock, which included thousands of cans of aerosols, which were exploding on all sides as the firefighters worked to extinguish the blaze. The fire was successfully contained in the chemist's shop and brought under control after four hours.

The seat of the fire was behind the counter in the dispensary, which was cleared of medicines every evening and contained little apart from some electrical appliances and wiring. A computer and a security light had been left switched on during the night. It was concluded that the most likely cause of the fire was an electrical fault.

## *1(d) Structural features that could lead to the spread of fire*

The most serious of the structural features that lead to the spread of fire are unprotected openings in compartment walls, floors and ceilings which allow the spread of flames, hot gases and smoke into adjacent areas. Not all of the features might be as obvious as holes around services that can easily be seen and identified.

When the risk assessment is carried out care should therefore be taken to identify:

- ducts without dampers;

- flues and redundant chimneys;

- voids behind panelling, above ceilings and below floors;

- unstopped holes around services;

- uncompartmented roof spaces;

- warped and ill-fitting doors;

- unprotected stairways;

- unprotected areas resulting from changes of use.

In some instances, for example in listed historic buildings, specialist advice may need to be taken regarding the likely presence of some of these features.

In some industrial premises, openings may be protected by fire-resistant roller shutters or similar devices and these should be checked periodically to ensure that they operate correctly and run freely. The areas beneath the shutters should be checked regularly to ensure that no obstructions are present which could compromise the correct operation of the device.

Openings around conveyor belts pose particular problems which are addressed in ways appropriate to the building and the operations that are being carried out. (Consideration of the materials from which the belts are constructed should not be forgotten.) The measures taken should, however, be assessed and checked regularly.

Further information about improving structural features may be found in the Fire Protection Association's *Design Guide for the Fire Protection of Buildings.*

## Stage 2: Identifying the people at risk

The people at risk may be staff, contractors, visitors or members of the public. Consideration should be given to the numbers of people visiting or working in each area, to ensure that the means of escape are adequate. The layout should also be assessed to ensure that the number of people working in inner rooms is kept

# Case history: Rapid spread of fire through unprotected roof voids

At 2029 hours on a January evening a passer-by discovered this fire in a school. The fire brigade was called and on their arrival the firefighters were confronted by a severe fire involving two classrooms. The fire was spreading rapidly, fuelled by gas supplies in a biology classroom and fanned by high winds. Jets were deployed in an attempt to prevent the fire from spreading to adjacent classrooms but once in the unprotected roof void, the flames spread even faster, causing crews to withdraw to a corridor.

The fire was brought under control two hours later, when the flames reached an area where there was firestopping between the roof and the suspended ceiling. By this time 16 fire appliances were involved in the firefighting operations and damage had affected 20 rooms. The loss was estimated to be £1.2 million.

On the day of the fire the children were on their Christmas holidays and the caretaker had left the building at 1630 hours, leaving everything secure and appliances all switched off.

The area of the school where the fire originated was not overlooked from any direction and had been subject to numerous incidents of vandalism. Investigators concluded that the most likely cause of the fire was malicious ignition.

to a minimum. Rearrangement of furniture, filing cabinets, room dividers or process plant must not result in the creation of lengthy dead-ends or increase beyond the acceptable limits the travel distance to a place of safety.

Particular note should be made where:

- sleeping accommodation is provided;

- large numbers of the public may be present;

- a significant number of very young or elderly people may be present;

- people may be unfamiliar with the layout of the building and the location of the exit routes;

- staff are working in areas where there is a specific risk, such as spray painting;

- people may have lengthy or tortuous escape routes;

- contractors are working up ladders or on scaffolding.

Consideration must always be given to the presence of people whose mobility, hearing or eyesight is impaired, even if only temporarily. Disabilities are not always apparent, people suffering from heart ailments and women who are in the latter stages of pregnancy, for example, may easily be overlooked when carrying out a risk assessment. Likewise, staff or visitors with a mental disability or mental illness should not be forgotten.

Contractors can also be overlooked and it is important that actions are taken to ensure that they can all be accounted for at a roll call, as well as for security reasons.

## Stage 3: Eliminating, controlling and avoiding the hazards

As stated earlier, risks may be eliminated, controlled, avoided or transferred. Examples of these principles are as follows:

### *Eliminating hazards*

Some hazards may be eliminated by prohibition or by changing procedures or practices. Smoking, for example, is a risk which may largely be eliminated and is now prohibited in most workplaces, although some employers make provision for people to smoke if they so wish. A designated smoking area should therefore be provided with adequate ashtrays, metal waste bins and with furniture that is only lightly upholstered.

The use of portable heaters should also be prohibited. If supplementary heating is necessary during periods of cold weather, suitable convector heaters should be provided and these should be secured to the floors or walls. Heaters fuelled by flammable liquids should not be allowed and those fuelled by gas cylinders should only be permitted when absolutely necessary.

Personal items of electrical equipment should generally be prohibited and only be used with the express permission of a person in authority and only after they have been subjected to the testing regime applied to other items of electrical equipment used in the premises.

If a fire does occur, its spread beyond the compartment of origin can be eliminated by adequate structural fire protection. This includes:

• firestopping around services;

• where there are ducts, installing automatic dampers in line with compartment walls;

• ensuring that fire doors are not distorted and are fitted with smoke seals and intumescent strips;

• ensuring, where necessary, that glazing is of the required standard.

### Controlling hazards

Although some risks may be eliminated, others may not, and instead have to be controlled.

Arson, which is an increasing threat to almost every business, may be reduced by denying intruders access to fuel, whether flammable liquids, raw materials or stock. It may also be controlled by carrying out a security survey and installing equipment such as security lighting, which has been found to be a particularly cost-effective deterrent. Denying access to roofs by pruning trees, and ensuring that all windows and doors are secured at the end of each working period are also simple, yet effective, measures against arson.

All deep fat fryers and similar cooking equipment should be fitted with thermostatic controls and should not be left unattended while in use. Stop valves for gas supplies should be fitted on exit routes so that they may be turned off safely in an emergency. Similarly, boilers should be protected by shut off valves operated by fusible links.

The risk of a fire caused by faulty electrical equipment, wiring and fittings has now largely been controlled by the implementation of the Electricity at Work Regulations 1989, which require all electrical equipment, leads and plugs to

# Case history: Six residents die in a residential care home

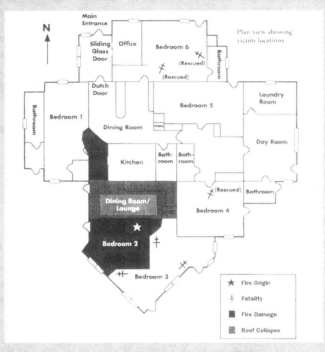

A fire in a care home for 22 residents in Broward County, Florida, USA, resulted in the death of six residents. At the time of the fire there were 19 residents and one member of staff in the building. At least 16 of the residents were described as schizophrenic and all took medications for their conditions. Some also had medical conditions that affected their mobility.

The management of the home used part-time employees who were not provided with fire safety training. The member of staff on duty at the time of the fire was primarily responsible for cleaning. As well as not having been trained in fire safety she had never participated in a fire drill.

The building had 13 rooms and 4 bathrooms laid out as shown in the plan. Although in the past there had been problems associated with the automatic fire detection and alarm installation and the link to the fire department, no records of the problem or any remedial action taken were recorded.

undergo regular visual inspection. Performing the periodic inspections of the wiring installed in the building that are set out in BS 7671: 2001: *Requirements for electrical installations. IEE Wiring Regulations. Sixteenth edition* also reduces the risk of an electrical fire occurring.

Rubbish should not be burnt on bonfires (bonfires should be prohibited); the hazard from waste materials should be controlled by removing them from the workplace at regular intervals (at least once each day) and placing them in a metal container (fitted with a lid) which is situated well away from the building.

Training of staff is also an important element of controlling the risks of fire, although it is for life safety purposes that it is principally undertaken. Staff who know how the manufacturing equipment works, how to use it safely, how to shut it down in an emergency and how to address problems or malfunctions as they arise are likely to be a great asset to a company in preventing the occurrence of fires and protecting life and property in the event of a fire occurring.

### Avoiding hazards

A third way of reducing the risk of fire is to avoid using processes which involve the use of heat, flammable liquids or easily ignitable solids.

In some instances, hot work – such as the burning off of paint – may be replaced by methods which do not involve the use of flames. Paint may be removed, for example, by methods involving non-combustible chemicals.

Processes which use flammable solvents should be carefully assessed; where acceptable non-flammable alternatives exist, and their use is economically viable, they should be used.

### Transferring hazards

When all of the fire hazards have been identified and appropriate actions taken to eliminate, control or avoid the risks, there will still be some hazards remaining which will have to be managed. These may be insured against, with the risks, in effect, being transferred to the insurer. The insurer may well review the situation or inspect the premises and make recommendations to reduce the risk of fire to what is considered to be as low a level as is practicable before accepting the residual risk.

The insured should inform the insurer if there are subsequently any changes to the nature of the risk in the premises. For example, the insurer should be informed if a manufacturing process is to be modified or new materials or fabrication procedures are to be introduced.

The insurer will expect the company to observe the legal requirements, Government and HSE guidance documents, appropriate British Standards and FPA Recommendations as a condition of the insurance.

## Stages 4 to 7

When the hazards have been identified, the existing fire safety provisions should be reviewed (stage 4 in carrying out the risk assessment) and any improvements necessary should be implemented. Chapter 5 will assist you to do this.

Stage 5 in the risk assessment is recording the findings, which is discussed in Chapter 6. Preparing an emergency plan for a large business (stage 6) is discussed in Chapter 10.

Finally, stage 7 is the carrying out of a periodic review of the assessment. No specific review period is indicated in the Regulatory Reform (Fire Safety) Order but it would be wise to review the assessment at least annually, perhaps at a time that a fire drill is undertaken. The assessment should also be reviewed if the nature of the work that is undertaken is changed, there have been changes in working practices or major changes in staff responsibilities.

# Coping with the residual risk

When the potential sources of ignition in the workplace have been identified, the combustible materials and people at risk have been identified and measures taken to eliminate, control or avoid the hazards, there will remain some risks which are inherent to the premises or the nature of the business. Suitable measures have therefore to be devised and implemented to ensure the safety of the workforce.

These measures will provide:

- adequate means of escape;

- suitable signs;

- escape lighting;

- a fire alarm and detection system;

- means for fighting a fire.

In some cases, costly solutions are not necessary. For example, the layout of the workplace may be rearranged so that staff work closer to the escape routes. But in other cases additional exits or escape routes may need to be provided or existing protected routes extended.

Having carried out the fire risk assessment outlined in Chapter 4, you will have some idea as to the relative level of fire risk that is inherent to your premises. In this chapter, reference will be made to 'low', 'normal' and 'high' levels of risk which are defined as:

- *Low:* where there is hardly any risk from fire, few combustible materials, no highly flammable substances, and virtually no sources of heat.

- *Normal:* where there are sufficient quantities of combustible materials and sources of heat to be of greater than low fire risk but where a fire would be likely to remain confined, or to spread but slowly.

- *High:* where there is a serious risk to life from fire, there are substantial quantities of combustible materials, there are any highly flammable substances, or there exists the likelihood of the rapid spread of fire, heat, or smoke.

# Means of escape

Whether your premises are of low, normal or high fire risk, the Regulatory Reform (Fire Safety) Order 2005 requires that suitable means of escape are provided. When deciding whether your escape routes are satisfactory you will need to consider:

- the findings of the fire risk assessment;

- the number of people who may be present, how familiar they are with their workplace and their ability to escape without assistance;

- where people may be if a fire occurs;

- the size of the workplace, its construction, contents and layout.

The general principle is that, other than in very small premises or those presenting low fire risk, there should be alternative means of escape such that, wherever a fire were to occur, people present could turn their backs on the flames and escape to a place of safety. Alternative routes should provide independent paths and protect people until they leave the building and reach that safe place.

## *The construction of escape routes*

Escape routes consist of a number of elements: corridors, lobbies and stairways. Each one of these should be constructed from suitable fire-resistant materials and be separated from the adjacent areas by fire-resisting doors. Thus as people escape from a building they should pass through areas progressively safer from the effects of the heat and smoke of the fire. It is therefore important that neither the materials from which the route is constructed, nor the surfaces of the walls or ceilings sustain a flame or emit significant amounts of smoke when heated.

When assessing your escape routes the construction and surface coatings of the routes should be checked. Brickwork, blockwork, concrete, plasterboard and woodwool slab are all suitable materials for the construction of the route. Some thermosetting plastics, thin vinyl and paper coverings are acceptable as surface coatings, but not heavy, flock wallpapers.

Any large area of combustible wall lining materials should be removed and replaced with suitable materials or treated to reduce the possibility of the linings contributing to the fire.

Notice boards on escape routes should be as small as possible and not carry large amounts of loose paper or fabrics. Ideally all notice boards should be sited away from escape routes.

As mentioned in Chapter 4, floor coverings should not be overlooked when assessing the hazards but carpeting or carpet tiles should never be used as wall coverings.

All holes around services such as pipes and cables should be stopped with fire-resistant material to prevent the spread of smoke and hot gases onto the escape routes.

Further advice on the fire resistance of escape routes is set out in Approved Document B to the Building Regulations 2000.

### If there is more than one escape route

The critical factor with regard to means of escape is that everyone present should be able to escape before the build up of smoke and heat endangers their lives. If more than one escape route is provided the maximum escape times should be:

1 minute for high fire risk areas;

3 minutes for normal fire risk areas;

5 minutes for low fire risk areas.

Remember that these figures include the time it takes people to react to hearing the alarm and also the time they may need to take to ensure that processing machinery is made safe before they leave their posts. Suitable reaction time must also be allowed for any people who are sleeping on the premises.

The escape times should be checked by carrying out a fire drill. One of the benefits of carrying out regular fire drills is to test that escape times can still be met and have not been adversely affected by changes in procedures or lack of staff training.

The travel time depends on a number of factors, but as a guide, where there is more than one escape route assume that:

12-25 metres can be travelled in 1 minute;

18-45 metres can be travelled in 3 minutes;

45-60 metres can be travelled in 5 minutes.

### If there is only one escape route

Multiple escape routes give staff confidence and if there is more than one route out of a building at least two routes should be designated as escape routes and be suitably protected and signed. If, however, your premises has a small floor area and a restricted number of floors a single escape route may well be satisfactory if all areas are assessed as being of normal or low fire risk.

Where 'dead-end' areas are present they should be kept as short as possible, and where escape can only be made in one direction it is important that staff are able to escape speedily. Thus, in these cases, the travel times and travel distances to a storey exit or a point where a second escape route becomes available, have to be reduced as follows:

30 seconds for high fire risk areas (6-12 metres);

1 minute for normal fire risk areas (9-25 metres);

3 minutes for low fire risk areas (12-45 metres).

Because of the dangers associated with 'dead-end' corridors, these areas should be constructed so as to provide at least 30 minutes fire resistance between the rooms and the corridor; the doors to the corridor should be to the same standard and be fitted with self-closers.

Where a 'dead-end' corridor meets a route along which escape is available in two directions the layout should be such that there is a door between the corridor and each of the alternative directions of travel. (See Figure 5.1.)

## The width of escape routes

As well as there being a sufficient number of escape routes they should be of an adequate width to allow all persons present to escape. Corridors should normally be at least 1 metre wide, although a width of at least 1.2 metres will be required by wheelchair users. Escape routes should not narrow along their length. Corridors that are over 30 metres long should be subdivided by doors in suitable frames that will resist the passage of fire, heat and smoke for at least 20 minutes.

Where escape routes pass across large areas of floor the route should be marked clearly on the floor by means such as paint or contrasting floor colouring so that attention is drawn to the route and so that it may be kept clear of obstructions.

A normal, single doorway 750mm wide will allow 40 people to escape each minute whereas a doorway 1 metre wide allows up to 80 people to escape per minute. Doors not less than 800mm wide will be required by wheelchair users. Where calculations show that larger numbers of people may have to escape per minute the width of a doorway should be increased by increments of 75mm for each 15 additional people. When calculating these figures it should always be assumed that one exit is not available because of the fire; for safety this has to be assumed to be the widest exit.

Particular consideration needs to be given to routes which may be used by staff or visitors with disabilities; additional advice in this respect is given in Chapter 6.

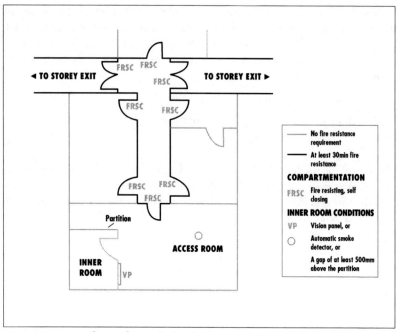

*Figure 5.1. Means of escape from a dead end or inner room.*

### Inner rooms

When designating escape routes the general rule should be that people travel to progressively lower areas of risk. Thus where the layout of the premises involves a 'room within a room' the outer room should not be an area of higher risk than the inner room.

Careful consideration needs also to be given to methods of alerting the occupants of the inner room to an outbreak of fire in the outer room. Therefore, there should be:

- a vision panel between the inner and outer rooms; or

- an automatic fire detector in the outer room; or

- there should be a gap of at least 500mm above the partition between the two rooms.

Where people have to sleep on the premises, inner rooms should not be used for this purpose.

## Stairways

Except in the case of very small businesses, stairways should not be less than 1 metre wide. Where the premises is of low or normal fire risk only one stairway need be provided if:

- the stairway does not serve more than three floors above or one floor below ground level; and

- the stairway is a 'protected' stairway. This means that the stairwell should be an enclosure constructed to provide at least 30 minutes fire resistance and with self-closing doors to this same standard; and

- access to the stairway is via a protected lobby or protected corridor other than on the top floor; and

- the stairway is of a sufficient width to accommodate the number of people needing to use it in an emergency; and

- the stairway leads directly to a place of safety in the open air.

The requirement regarding the need for protected lobbies does not apply to premises of low fire risk or those of normal fire risk where the areas opening onto the stairway are already protected by an automatic fire detection system or a sprinkler installation connected to the fire alarm system.

In small, low risk workplaces a single, unprotected stairway may be satisfactory as a means of escape if:

- the stairway provides access between the ground and first floor or the ground and the basement only; and

- an exit can be reached in the times relating to single escape routes given above; and

- the access to the stairway is clearly visible from all areas on each floor; and

- the stairway discharges less than 6 metres from an exit leading to open air at ground floor level.

Where external stairways are provided, all doors (other than those at the head of the stair), any part of the external envelope of the building and all areas of glazing within 1.8 metres horizontally or 9 metres vertically of such stairways should be of at least 30 minutes fire resistance to ensure that the escape route is protected from smoke and flames and can be used safely without endangering the lives of people escaping.

The door to the final exit should be easily and immediately openable without the use of a key or code. In some areas security considerations will require that the doors are secured, but they must not be locked. Suitable hardware – such as push bars or, where a limited number of people may have to escape, latches operable by a handle provided only on the inside of the door – may be fitted.

So that people can escape quickly, doors on escape routes should open in the direction of travel where:

- more than 50 people may have to pass through the doorway;

- the door is at, or near to the foot of the stairs;

- the door serves an area of high fire risk;

- the building is used as a place of assembly, such as a conference centre or an exhibition or concert hall.

In cases where it is impractical for self-closing fire doors to be closed all the time, they may in some instances be held open by an automatic door release mechanism arranged to release the door on the:

- failure of the mains power;

- actuation of the fire alarm;

- actuation of one of the smoke detectors installed each side of the doorway;

- application of manual pressure.

### Alternative forms of escape routes

Other means of escape which, although not normally deemed by enforcing authorities as being suitable for use by members of the public, may nevertheless be used by a limited number of trained, fit members of staff include:

- portable, foldaway, vertical, raking or throw-out ladders;

- window exits;

- wicket doors and gates;

- wall and floor hatches;

- rolling shutters;

- folding, sliding and up-and-over doors.

Escalators may be used as means of escape when they stop automatically when the fire alarm operates.

### *Items which should not be located on escape routes*

No items which restrict the width of the escape route or increase the hazard of the area should be allowed on escape routes. Thus corridors, stairways, landings and lobbies should be kept clear of:

- portable heaters of all types;

- fixed lights or heaters incorporating flames or radiant bars;

- gas cylinders;

- boilers, unless installed in suitable fire-resistant housings;

- cooking appliances, including toasters and microwave ovens;

- electrical appliances, including photocopiers and shredders;

- vending and games machines.

Furniture should be kept to a minimum and should not reduce the width of the route. Any furniture necessary, such as in a reception area, should comply with the Furniture and Furnishings (Fire) (Safety) Regulations 1988.

Artificial foliage, shrubs and decorations should only be placed on escape routes if the supplier satisfies you that they have behaved satisfactorily when subjected to the flame ignition source of BS 5852: *Fire tests for furniture.*

## Signs

In most workplaces of normal or low fire risk only those escape routes which are not in common use need be signed with the running man, open door and arrow pictograms. However, in areas to which the public have access, all escape routes should be signed. Signs should be displayed unambiguously along the length of the route so that it may be followed without delay.

Escape routes should no longer be signed 'fire exit' without pictograms, although this wording may be used alongside the pictograms.

Examples of mandatory signs relating to fire doors are shown in Figure 5.2. Signs indicating the location of firefighting equipment should be provided if it is not immediately visible.

## Escape lighting

In the event of a fire there may be poor visibility or the mains power supply might fail. It is therefore necessary to provide suitable emergency escape lighting so that the escape routes may be identified and followed.

## Mandatory signs

| Sign | Meaning | Location |
|------|---------|----------|
| **Fire door keep shut** | Do not prevent self-closing fire door from closing. | At eye level on both faces of each leaf of self-closing fire doorsets. |
| **Fire door keep locked** | Keep fire door locked shut when not in use. | At eye level on the outside of each leaf of fire doorsets required to be kept locked, e.g. store cupboards on protected routes. |
| **Automatic fire door keep clear** | Keep area clear of obstructions that might prevent the operation of an automatic fire door or shutter. | At eye level on or near a fire door or shutter that closes automatically in the event of a fire. |
| **Fire escape keep clear** | Keep area clear of obstructions which may impede escape. | On escape routes at points where obstructions may occur, e.g. on the exterior face of a final exit door. |
| **Secure door open when premises are occupied** | Door to be secured in the open position so that escape will not be impeded on final exits. | At eye level on doors or gates that may impede escape if not secured in the open position, e.g. inward opening doors. |

*Figure 5.2. Examples of mandatory fire safety signs.*

Emergency escape lighting should be provided:

- so that the fire exit signs are visible;

- in corridors without windows or without the benefit of borrowed light (such as that from street lamps);

- to illuminate changes in level of the floor or changes in direction;

- in unlit areas such as basements;

- in large open-plan office areas;

- to ensure that hazardous processes can be shut down safely;

- on external escape routes to the final place of safety if necessary.

Emergency escape lighting installations should comply with the requirements of BS 5266: 2005: *Emergency lighting. Code of practice for the emergency lighting of premises.*

Not all premises, however, require such installations; in small businesses, of low or normal fire risk, a supply of torches may be adequate providing that staff are familiar with their location and that the batteries are checked periodically. Spare batteries should be readily available.

## Fire alarm and detection systems

Complex, state of the art fire detection and alarm systems are not required in all workplaces. In many small businesses there is no need for an automatic fire detection installation at all if the alarm can be simply and effectively raised by word of mouth. What is important, however, is that all of the staff are aware of the procedures and react correctly in an emergency.

### The fire alarm

Where only a few staff are at work and they are all in the same area, word of mouth can be adequate to raise the alarm. In somewhat larger businesses a handbell or rotary gong may be needed to ensure that the alarm is audible throughout the premises above the day-to-day background noise level. This manual equipment should be located on escape routes and, if it is not immediately noticeable, a suitable sign should be provided.

It is not acceptable for the telephone to be used as a means of raising the alarm, even in small businesses.

New electric fire alarm installations should comply with BS 5839: 2002: *Fire detection and fire alarm systems for buildings:* Part 1: *Code of practice for system design, installation, commissioning and maintenance,* but if your existing installation does not comply with this standard it is acceptable, provided that it is properly maintained. The break glass fire alarm call points should be situated on escape routes. The type of sound produced by the alarm is not critical, the sounders may be bells or warblers, provided that the audibility is adequate and the sound of the alarm is distinctive with regard to the background noises in the workplace.

The responsible person in large buildings and premises to which the public have access should consider installing a public address system or voice alarm installation so that instructions can be given to people leaving the building. Research has shown that this form of assistance is particularly effective, leading to people responding much more quickly than just to the sound of the alarm.

### Automatic fire detection

In large or complex workplaces, or those where a fire could break out in an unoccupied area, consideration may be given to installing an automatic fire detection (AFD) system. This will allow the alarm to be raised at the earliest opportunity, giving the maximum time for staff to escape and the fire to be fought with portable equipment.

Indeed, it is a consequence of the Workplace Regulations introduced in 1997 that the occupiers of all workplaces consider the benefits of installing appropriate fire detection equipment.

Managers of large premises should consult their insurer and the enforcing authority if consideration is being given to the installation of AFD. The provision of AFD may have the effect of reducing the risk category of the premises from, for example, a high to a normal risk.

The provision of an automatic fire detection system is particularly advisable in premises where people sleep. Although two or more interlinked domestic smoke alarms would be suitable for premises such as a small guest house, domestic alarms are not generally appropriate for commercial or industrial premises as the detectors would not be connected to the main fire alarm panel and the alarm may not be heard throughout the building.

Where an AFD system is installed it should be linked to the fire alarm to form a single integrated system.

## False alarm reduction

As the number of fire alarm and detection systems installed in premises has increased there has been a related increase in the number of 'false alarms', now designated as Unwanted Fire Signals (UwFS) by the authorities who have to respond to them. An UwFS may be defined as 'a fire signal resulting from a cause other than fire'.

The authorities' response to such UwFS from remotely monitored fire alarm systems has been identified as a major drain on resources and led to brigades making alterations to their level of response to such signals – i.e. reducing the number of pumps initially attending. This situation could clearly have an effect on the speed with which a real fire may be tackled and hence the scale and scope of subsequent property damage and business interruption losses.

In order to address this issue on a national basis the Chief Fire Officers' Association (CFOA) has introduced a policy which it believes will assist in reducing the number of false alarms from remotely monitored fire alarms and also provide end-users and fire authorities with a nationally recognised protocol and standard in this regard. It outlines three levels of response based on the number of false alarms received from each individual system on a rolling 12-month period basis. Hence, repeat offenders may well find that the local fire authority may eventually withdraw response to remotely monitored alarm systems, attending only once they receive confirmation that fire or smoke has been seen.

It is therefore essential that the number of false alarms triggering a response from the local fire service via a remotely monitored system are reduced to an absolute minimum. Further detailed guidance on the steps that can be taken to reduce false alarms, together with a requirement that all such events be recorded, can be found in BS 5839: Part 1: 2002. A thorough investigation should be made of the cause of each false alarm and appropriate steps taken to remedy the situation.

## Firefighting equipment

It is a requirement of the Fire Safety Order that, where necessary, premises have suitable means available for fighting a fire. Equipment is classified according to the class of fire on which it is effective:

- Class A – fires involving solid materials such as paper, wood and textiles.

- Class B – fires involving flammable liquids (including cooking oils and fats in kitchens).

- Class C – fires involving gases.

- Class D – fires involving metals.

- Class F – fires involving modern high temperature cooking oils.

In addition, consideration has to be given to the fires involving live electrical equipment.

## Portable fire extinguishers

In practice, extinguishers suitable for only Class A and Class B risks are provided since fires involving gases (Class C) should not be fought using extinguishers until the supply of gas is turned off, otherwise there is a danger of causing an explosion. Special training and equipment is required to fight fires involving burning metals.

There are four types of extinguishers commonly available which, until the beginning of 1997, were coloured as follows:

- water – red;

- foam – cream;

- carbon dioxide – black;

- dry powder – blue.

The introduction of BS EN 3: *Portable fire extinguishers* has resulted in all extinguishers being coloured red with a zone of colour of up to 5% of the extinguisher body, corresponding to the colours above to indicate the extinguishing agent. While it is not necessary to replace all of the extinguishers in the workplace, replacements should be phased so that all extinguishers in each working area or fire point have the same colouring scheme. The colours of fire extinguishers are illustrated on the inside of the front cover of this book.

Although some small fires may be fought using something as simple as a bucket of water, a fire extinguisher allows the same amount of water to be used in a more efficient manner. In many small workplaces a single extinguisher may be all that needs be provided.

Class F extinguishers are a relatively new development. They should comply with BS 7937: 2000 and have an identification colour of canary yellow covering between 3 and 10% of the extinguisher body.

The extinguisher must, however, be of a size that will be effective if used by a trained person. Extinguishers are therefore given ratings for comparison purposes. The rating for extinguishers suitable for use on Class A fires are based on the size of a specified wooden crib fire that can be extinguished. Class B extinguishers are rated according to their performance when used to fight liquid pool fires. Extinguishers most commonly encountered have 13A or 34B ratings.

In general, the number of extinguishers necessary is determined by the nature of the risk and the size of the floor area. The types of extinguishers suitable for various risks are indicated above while the numbers required are determined as follows:

- one extinguisher per 200 square metres of floor area;

- at least one extinguisher per floor;

- no one should have to travel more than 30 metres to reach an extinguisher.

Extinguishers provided for a particular hazard should be located near that hazard, other extinguishers should be located on escape routes, preferably near the exits. They should be hung on hooks on the wall or placed on stands so that staff become familiar with where to find them. The extinguishers should be positioned so that the carrying handle is about 1 metre off the floor.

Firefighting equipment such as extinguishers, fire alarm call points and fire action notices should be grouped together to form fire points on escape routes. Where the layout of the buildings repeats from floor to floor, the fire points should be located at the same points on each floor.

Where they are not immediately visible, the location of extinguishers should be indicated by means of signs.

Where necessary, extinguishers should be protected from the effects of the weather.

It is advisable to purchase only extinguishers which are approved and certified by an independent, third-party certification body.

## *Other firefighting equipment*

As distinct from a water fire extinguisher, a hose reel should be capable of providing an endless supply of extinguishing agent. Although there is no legal requirement to install hose reels, consideration should be given to providing them in areas such as warehouses and large storerooms. If hose reels are provided they should be located on escape routes and if they are not conspicuous, their presence should be indicated with a sign. Notices adjacent to the hose reels should indicate their mode of action and staff should be trained in their use.

Staff training should emphasise safety, to ensure that the user does not attempt to remain in the area concerned to fight the fire longer than would be wise. Also there is a danger that if the firefighting is unsuccessful the abandoned hose may hold open fire doors and allow the fire to spread.

Existing hose reels should not be removed from premises without the agreement of the local fire brigade and the insurers of the property.

Some high fire risk premises such as industrial plants also provide large capacity wheeled foam or dry powder extinguishers pressurised by carbon dioxide cylinders or compressed air.

Fire blankets are suitable for small fires involving flammable liquids and for extinguishing burning clothing. Consideration should be given to providing fire blankets near the entrances to kitchens.

## Fixed firefighting installations

The most common form of fixed firefighting system is a water sprinkler installation. Such installations can be very effective, not only in detecting a fire, but in raising the alarm and fighting the flames. Any sprinkler or other form of automatic firefighting system should be linked to the fire alarm system for the premises.

Like AFD systems, fixed firefighting installations may have the effect of reducing the risk category of a building from high to normal risk. The enforcing authority and your insurer should also be contacted before a decision is taken to install such a system.

Water sprinklers, in common with gaseous firefighting systems used to protect computer suites, deluge systems in the chemical industry and other forms of fixed installations, have to be carefully designed to meet the needs of the risk and comply with the appropriate technical standards. Thus, they should be installed by competent companies such as those identified in the annual Loss Prevention Certification Board (LPCB) *List of Approved Fire and Security Products and Services*. If material alterations are subsequently made to the premises specialist advice should be sought from the installers.

# Management procedures

There are two main ways of ensuring the safety of staff in the event of fire. The first is to provide physical measures such as suitable passive features (fire doors, compartmentation and so on) and active installations (automatic fire detection and fire suppression systems) as may be required by legislation, through a fire risk assessment or as otherwise determined as being cost effective. The second is to introduce management procedures to minimise the remaining risk.

Problems that are commonly countered by the introduction of appropriate management procedures include:

- assisting people with disabilities to escape;

- liaising with contractors;

- good housekeeping;

- maintenance and testing of fire safety equipment;

- record keeping;

- staff training.

It must be stressed that model management procedures cannot be set out in this, or any other, publication. The procedures have to be designed for a particular company, with their working practices, type of premises and nature and number of staff in mind. The following sections, however, outline some of the principles which should generally be incorporated into the relevant policy documents and staff training programmes.

Record keeping, maintenance and testing of fire safety equipment, and staff training was in the past a requirement of the fire certificate, where one was issued for the premises. With the introduction of the Regulatory Reform (Fire Safety) Order, these measures remain important and should be key features of the fire risk assessment for the workplace. In addition, there remains a duty on the employer to maintain the workplace in an efficient state and in good repair. This is discussed further in the housekeeping section below.

## Assisting people with disabilities to escape

As has already been indicated in an earlier chapter, although the phrase 'people with disabilities' normally conjures up pictures of people in wheelchairs, the scope of the subject is much wider. People with sensory impairments, medical conditions which may result in slow or difficult movement, people with mental illness or disability and staff or visitors with forms of temporary impairment, such as legs in plaster and late stages of pregnancy, are also particularly at risk in the event of fire. It should be remembered that even a minor injury to a normally fit member of staff may result in that person being unable to react as promptly as normal in the event of the fire alarm sounding.

Many of the people just mentioned will be able to use the normal means of escape without difficulty but, because of the amount of space required to turn a wheelchair, special consideration has to be given to escape routes where they may be used. Refuges, evacuation lifts and other facilities may also have to be provided. Guidance regarding means for access and escape are set out in BS 5588: *Fire precautions in the design, construction and use of buildings*: Part 8: *Code of practice for means of escape for disabled people* and Approved Document M to the Building Regulations 2000: *Access to and Use of Buildings*. Reference should be made to these publications for detailed advice but continuing attention needs to be given to the width of gangways in offices, filing and storage areas where furniture and stored materials may be moved on a day-to-day basis as well as ensuring that protected escape routes are kept completely clear of obstructions.

Every employer has a duty of care towards their staff and others who may be in their premises, including visitors and contractors, however fit or unwell they might be. It is therefore the employer's responsibility, wherever circumstances allow, to be aware of anyone who may need assistance to leave their premises in an emergency, and to plan in advance such measures as may be necessary to ensure the safety of anyone with any form of disability who may be present.

So that suitable assistance can be provided managers should know:

- how many disabled staff or visitors are on the premises;

- the nature of their disabilities;

- the areas where they normally work or visit and hence the refuges in which they might be located.

The Disability Discrimination Act 1995 requires that provisions are available for disabled persons to have reasonable access to premises. The Act, however, embodies no equivalent requirements with regard to egress from the buildings. The principle of 'reasonableness' is the test that should be applied when considering means of escape. If provisions are made to allow people of all abilities to enter an area, the responsible person for the premises should make such plans as may be necessary to ensure that everyone can leave the premises safely in the event of an emergency.

Wherever possible an inclusive design approach should be adopted, catering for everyone in the building rather than considering separate means of escape for disabled people. Where this has to adopted, however, a personal emergency evacuation plan should be devised for people that are routinely in the premises. This should be done in consultation with each person involved.

To ensure a safe and orderly evacuation in an emergency, procedures should be in place, with plans being rehearsed and all staff who may be involved receiving suitable training. This will include all fire marshals who will have a key role to ensure that disabled people who may be present are assisted to reach a place of safety, normally the fire assembly point.

In public buildings where groups of people with physical or mental disabilities may visit, managers should ensure that they are accompanied by a suitable number of carers who should be made aware of the location of the refuges and the procedures for evacuating the premises. In the workplace, designated fire wardens should be identified and trained to assist specific members of staff in an emergency where a 'buddy' system is not in operation.

### Evacuation lifts

The provision of lifts specially designed to be used by disabled people to escape in the event of fire is particularly beneficial and may reduce the amount of physical assistance that has to be provided by able-bodied staff. They may also be of more general use, particularly to the occupants of high rise buildings; suitably protected lifts will also be of service to the fire brigade for firefighting purposes. The design of evacuation lifts for disabled people are described in BS 5588: *Fire precautions in the design and construction of buildings:* Part 8: *Code of practice for means of escape for disabled people.* The construction of lifts for firefighting purposes, which may also be used to evacuate disabled people, is set out in BS 5588: Part 5: *Code of practice for firefighting stairs and lifts.*

Where protected lifts are provided, priority use of these should be given to people with a disability in an emergency. Unless a lift is specially designed for such a purpose, it should not be used by anyone in case of fire and should be programmed to return, normally to the ground floor, on actuation of the fire alarm.

In a small number of large premises, however, there may be lift shafts at opposite ends of a building. In such a case, it may be possible to continue to use one of these for evacuating the building if there is suitable compartmentation of the premises. In these cases the lift in the end of the building where the fire is located should return to ground level, while disabled people move horizontally to the lift that can remain operational. The procedures for using lifts in this way, however, should be carefully planned in conjunction with the fire brigade and be subject to a comprehensive risk assessment before being adopted.

In an analogous fashion it may often be possible to continue to use escalators for evacuating shops and similar premises in an emergency.

Although stairlifts are designed for access during normal conditions, they should not be used as a means of escape in the event of fire as not only is there a danger of the lift failing, but it will also obstruct the stairway for use by able-bodied people.

### *Refuges*

Ideally, all disabled people should be able to reach a place of safety without assistance. In practice, however, assistance is often required, especially to use stairways, and so refuges should be provided on all floors, except those only occupied by plant rooms. Refuges need not be provided in small buildings where the travel distance to the final exit is limited.

Where a refuge is provided, the employer's responsibility does not end at this point. A refuge is not an area to which people with a disability may be taken and left to be rescued by the fire brigade, it is the employer's responsibility to ensure the safe evacuation of the premises and reliance must not be made on the fire brigade to effect this. In an emergency, the fire brigade will rescue people, but these actions take priority over firefighting and thus until they are satisfied that everyone is accounted for, the fire brigade may have to delay firefighting operations.

Thus, while a refuge may be valuable as a resting point, allowing able-bodied staff to pass, it is not the final solution to the problem. Everyone with a disability who is regularly in the premises should be consulted when evacuation plans are being devised as they often have a significant contribution to make to the strategy that should be adopted to assist their egress from the building. The latter should be recorded as the person's personal emergency evacuation plan.

No one should ever be left alone at a refuge, other than in exceptional circumstances; they should be accompanied by their carer, 'buddy' or designated fire warden.

As already indicated, a refuge is an area where a person in a wheelchair, or with another form of difficulty, may rest or wait in relative safety for a short while, allowing others to use the route normally until assistance is available from staff, the stairs may be used safely, or the evacuation lift is available.

Refuges may be present on escape stairways and outside evacuation lifts; they should either be part of, or open onto protected stairways so that an area of higher risk does not have to be entered subsequently. Where refuges are in compartments, these should be of at least 30 minutes' fire resistance, fitted with doors of the same standard.

In large buildings there should be a system of two-way communication provided in the refuges so that anyone waiting may make themselves known to the person responsible for the evacuation of the premises. Where necessary, people waiting in refuges should be reassured and kept informed of the circumstances using the communications arrangements provided.

Refuges should be clearly identified by appropriate fire safety signs and should be kept free of obstructions. Where a refuge is in a stairway or lobby a blue and white 'refuge keep clear' sign should be displayed.

Where evacuation chairs or similar devices are provided to assist in the evacuation, staff who are expected to use them in an emergency should receive suitable training and rehearse the procedures with the people whom they are expected to assist. The procedures should be subject to appropriate health and safety assessments, especially in respect of lifting and the weight that staff may be expected to carry.

## Procedures in case of fire

It is important that all disabled staff are aware of facilities, such as evacuation lifts, that have been provided for their convenience and are consulted during the development of arrangements for their safe evacuation. In premises that are open to the public, or where disabled visitors may be present, the fire wardens should be made aware, as part of their training, of the actions that they should take to assist them. Even where disabled staff are familiar with the surroundings, they should not be left alone in refuges or elsewhere; designated helpers should assist them according to the pre-planned arrangements.

The plan should also provide for a fire warden to check the first-aid room and contact the person responsible for the evacuation if further assistance is required.

All disabled staff, whether temporary or permanent, should take part in fire drills so that they can gain confidence in the measures that have been provided and also so that any problems, perhaps relating to their impact on the behaviour and escape times of other staff who are evacuating the areas, can be resolved. These issues should be considered at the debriefing following the drills.

Where people are newly employed or are returning to work with limited mobility for whatever reason, consideration should be given to how best to provide for them before they commence or return to work.

Where there is sleeping accommodation on the premises, such as in hotels, visitors with disabilities should be encouraged to make themselves known to the management or reception staff so that they can be given purpose-designed rooms or rooms on the lower floors of the building and can be provided with assistance if required in an emergency.

In buildings where there is a two-stage fire alarm, all disabled staff should commence evacuation immediately the first alarm sounds. There should be no delay in evacuating people with a disability from the premises, and the minimum of pauses for rest in refuges, if the risk of fire or smoke spread is high.

In the event of fire, disabled people should be evacuated in the following order:

1. from the floor on which the fire has occurred;

2. from the floor immediately above the floor on which the fire has occurred;

3. the upper floors should then be evacuated from the top floor downwards;

4. finally, the floors beneath the fire should be evacuated from the upper floor downwards.

Some circumstances may occur, however, which require this plan to be modified.

In many instances, a person with a disability may not be immediately apparent and where there may be people present with hearing or sight impairments these problems should also be addressed in the emergency procedures. Staff or regular visitors with severe difficulties should each have a personal emergency evacuation plan and consideration should be given to the provision of beacons in certain areas or vibrating pagers to raise the alarm in case of fire. Induction loops should not be relied on to raise the alarm of fire for people with hearing difficulties.

In the case of staff or regular visitors with sight problems, a personal emergency evacuation plan should again be formulated, taking into account the guide dog, if present, which should be left in the control of the handler. The procedures for assisting the person from the building should again be rehearsed taking into consideration the desires of the person involved, who is normally best guided with their hand on the shoulder of their helper.

Where staff or visitors may suffer from visual impairment consideration should be given to the provision of tactile surfaces to enable escape routes to be identified easily.

## *Liaising with contractors*

Many large fires occur when contractors are at work either building or refurbishing premises. Building procedures, by their very nature, increase the risk of fire by introducing additional combustible materials and potential sources of ignition. By far the biggest problem involves the carrying out of procedures involving hot work. This may involve the use of:

- cutting or welding equipment;

- blowlamps, blowtorches and hot-air paint strippers;

- angle grinders, cutting discs and abrasive wheels;

- tar boilers.

The use of such equipment will, in most cases, increase the risk of a fire occurring. In order to control this risk, managers should ensure that hot work is carried out under a hot-work permit scheme, unless there is no threat to nearby property.

The permit scheme should ensure that:

- before work commences the area is cleared of combustible material, and combustible flooring, or other items that cannot be removed are covered or screened with a non-combustible material;

- combustible material is also removed from the opposite sides of walls, partitions and other heat-conducting elements in the immediate vicinity of the work;

- suitable fire extinguishers are available, with staff trained in their use;

- a watch for fire is maintained while the work is in progress;

- any gas cylinders are secured in a vertical position and are fitted with regulators and flashback arrestors;

- tar boilers are only taken onto roofs in exceptional circumstances when a non-combustible heat insulating base must be provided, spilled material must be easily controlled and the gas cylinders must be at least 3m from the burner;

- all areas where work has taken place must be thoroughly examined one hour after work has finished.

Any work that is being undertaken should be carried out following the guidance set out in the Joint Code of Practice, *Fire Prevention on Construction Sites*, published by the Construction Confederation and the Fire Protection Association. This should ensure that the hazards associated with temporary accommodation, waste materials, smoking, temporary electrical supplies and the use of flammable liquids and gases are minimised.

In the case of a small project that is being managed in-house, the guidance given in that document should also be observed, but in this case careful management of the contractors' operations needs to be undertaken to ensure, for example, that hot work is not being undertaken by one contractor at the same time that another is using flammable adhesives in the same area.

When redecoration and similar minor works are being undertaken close liaison should be maintained with contractors to ensure that escape routes are kept free of obstructions or, if scaffold towers, for example, are built on an escape route, alternative routes are provided and signed.

Adequate access to the site for the fire brigade must be provided at all times that contractors are at work. Close liaison should be maintained with the brigade if problems are likely to arise.

## Good housekeeping

Good housekeeping in relation to fire safety refers to the need for tidiness and cleanliness and tends to promote efficient working practices as well as reducing the risk of a fire occurring. Good housekeeping results in the combustible materials which have to be in the workplace being controlled and this complements stock control measures which regulate the amount of such materials that are present.

One of the most important tasks is the regular inspection of escape routes to ensure that they are free of obstruction. Special attention should be paid to parts of these routes which are in the vicinity of loading bays or delivery points. Where necessary, indelible lines should be marked on the floor to indicate areas which must be kept clear.

As well as ensuring that there are no obstructions, the Fire Safety Order requires that the workplace is maintained in good repair. This is most important with regards to the escape routes. Stairs should be free of tripping hazards and any external escape stairs should be inspected regularly to ensure that they are free from rust as well as overhanging shrubs and trees. In winter months it may be necessary to clear external routes, including the stairways, of snow several times a day. Surface covering materials should be repaired when necessary and should not be peeling, as peeled wallpaper presents a higher fire risk than paper that is stuck securely to the substrate. In a similar way, the covers of chairs should not be allowed to remain ripped, exposing the padding beneath.

## *Control of waste materials*

All waste, especially accumulations of combustible materials, should be removed from the workplace at regular intervals and placed in a metal container situated in a safe location outside the premises. The container should ideally be fitted with a lid and thus be a large bin or covered skip. Where large amounts of materials such as cardboard accumulate, consideration should be given to the provision of a compactor to reduce the volume of the material that is being stored.

Waste materials should not be burnt on bonfires even if it is thought that this can be done safely. Contractors should also be made aware that bonfires are prohibited.

Empty gas cylinders should be housed in a purpose-built store and flammable liquid containers should similarly be stored, with their caps on, in a suitable area.

Weeds, grass and shrubs should be kept trimmed, especially during summer months, to prevent a build-up of dry tinder. Mechanical trimming should be employed rather than chemical treatment with weed killers as some of the latter can result in the undergrowth becoming even more easily ignited.

## *Smoking*

In some businesses a total prohibition on smoking is impractical, even if the majority of staff agree with the policy. A solution adopted by many companies is therefore to have a designated area where smoking is permitted; this area should be furnished with chairs complying with the Furniture and Furnishings (Fire) (Safety) Regulations 1988 and having limited amounts of padded upholstery. An appropriate number of ashtrays should also be provided.

Such an approach is not practicable in premises open to the general public so in these buildings a careful inspection should be made after they have been closed at the end of each day to ensure that no smouldering fires remain.

## Maintenance and testing

The Regulatory Reform (Fire Safety) Order 2005 requires that 'Where necessary, in order to safeguard the safety of relevant persons the responsible person must ensure that the premises and any facilities, equipment and devices provided... are subject to a suitable system of maintenance and are maintained in an efficient state, in efficient working order and in good repair'.

When equipment is selected it should be suitable for the purpose intended. In order to ensure that it is kept in good working order it should be properly tested and maintained. As a general rule it is advisable that all fire protection installations and equipment are serviced annually by a competent contractor.

| EQUIPMENT | INTERVAL | ACTION REQUIRED |
|---|---|---|
| Fire detection and alarm installations, including self-contained alarms and manually operated devices. | Weekly | ◇ Check for state of repair and operation.<br>◇ Repair or replace defective parts.<br>◇ Test operation, including self-contained alarms and manually operated devices. |
| | Annually | ◇ Service and test by a competent engineer.<br>◇ Clean self-contained smoke alarms and replace batteries. |
| Emergency lighting, self-contained units and torches. | Weekly | ◇ Check torches and replace batteries if required.<br>◇ Repair or replace defective units. |
| | Monthly | ◇ Check all lights and torches for state of repair and correct functioning. |
| | Annually | ◇ Service and test by a competent engineer. Replace batteries in torches. |
| Firefighting equipment, including hose reels. | Weekly | ◇ Check all equipment for correct installation and apparent function. |
| | Annually | ◇ Service and test by a competent engineer. |

*Figure 6.1. Users' maintenance checklist*

Such contractors may be identified by third-party assurances from accredited organisations. Thus, for example, fire extinguishers should be serviced by a company registered with the British Approvals for Fire Equipment (BAFE) under their approvals scheme SP10: *Contract Maintenance of Portable Extinguishers*. There is no legal obligation to use such contractors but doing so is good practice and will receive the backing of your insurers. The Fire Protection Association or your local fire brigade will be able to provide further details.

Similarly, all electrical appliances should be maintained under the provisions of the Electricity at Work Regulations 1989 to reduce the risk of electric shocks and fires occurring.

Some fire safety provisions, such as the fastenings on doors on the fire escape route, may be checked and tested adequately by a competent member of staff.

All staff should participate in checking the fire alarm system and should be encouraged to report areas in which the fire alarm is inaudible or sounders fail to operate during the weekly fire alarm tests.

The exact nature of the maintenance requirements will vary from building to building depending on the equipment provided but a general guide to what should be undertaken is given in Figure 6.1.

## Record keeping

One consequence of the introduction of the Regulatory Reform (Fire Safety) Order 2005 – which continues the trend set by the amendment of the Management of Health and Safety at Work Regulations 1999 by the Fire Precautions (Workplace) Regulations 1997 (as amended) – is that if the employer employs five or more people, the fire risk assessment should be recorded. The record should indicate the significant findings of the assessment and any group of persons identified as being especially at risk. The fire risk assessment should be a written document with a note of who carried out the assessment and on what date. The Fire Safety Order does not specify the format that is required; the checklists in Chapter 9 and Appendix B could be used as the basis for the record and, in the case of a small business, little else may be necessary.

It is a requirement of the Fire Safety Order that the workplace and any equipment and devices provided for fire safety purposes are maintained in an efficient state, in effective working order and good repair. Although the Fire Safety Order does not require that records are kept, it is clearly in the interest of the responsible person to do so. This will be a useful aide memoire and will show, in the event of a visit by the local fire authority, that fire safety is taken seriously by the management of the company.

The Fire Safety Order indicates that the workplace shall be maintained; this includes the need for the escape routes to be inspected regularly to ensure that they are free of obstructions and the final exits may be easily opened. Records of these inspections should also be kept.

The fire protection equipment that has to be maintained and tested includes the means for fighting fire (both portable and fixed equipment), smoke control or smoke venting facilities (if these are installed), and emergency escape lighting installations. There are no standard forms that must be used to record details of the maintenance and, although some small businesses may choose to use a ruled exercise book, larger companies tend to use a log book such as that produced by the Fire Protection Association. Figures 6.2, 6.3 and 6.4 are examples of record sheets taken from that publication.

Records should include the date on which the work was undertaken and by whom. Any defects should be recorded and the action taken to remedy the problems, together with the date and the person undertaking the task, should also be noted.

Staff training records (see Figure 6.3) should include:

- the date of the instruction or exercise;
- the nature of the instruction, training or fire drill;
- the duration of the sessions;
- the name of the person giving the training; and
- the names of the people receiving the training.

If a fire drill (see Figure 6.4) reveals a major defect in the procedures, means of escape, including the signs, means of opening the doors or the emergency escape lighting, consideration should be given to repeating the exercise as soon as the defects have been remedied.

## Staff training

There is a legal requirement to provide fire safety training for all staff under the Regulatory Reform (Fire Safety) Order 2005 and the Management of Health and Safety at Work Regulations 1999.

As described in Chapter 2, the Fire Safety Order requires the responsible person to ensure that their employees are provided with adequate safety training when they are first employed and if they become exposed to new or increased risks through the introduction of new equipment or a new system of work, for example. The training should include instruction on the appropriate precautions and actions to be taken by employees to safeguard themselves and others on the premises, be provided in a manner appropriate to the risk identified by the risk assessment, be repeated periodically, adapted when circumstances change, and carried out in working hours.

Similarly, Regulation 13(2) of the Management of Health and Safety at Work Regulations 1999 requires that every employer 'shall ensure that his employees are provided with adequate health and safety training'. This training must include matters of general fire safety. Furthermore, the employee should be given this training:

- on being recruited into the employer's undertaking (induction training);
- on being exposed to new or increased risks.

The Regulations require that the training shall:

- be repeated periodically where appropriate;
- be adapted to take account of any new or changed risks to the health and safety of the employees concerned;
- take place during working hours.

## EMERGENCY LIGHTING: ROUTINE MONTHLY CHECKS

| Date | Equipment tested | Faults and remedial action | Signed |
|---|---|---|---|
| | | | |
| | | | |
| | | | |
| | | | |
| | | | |
| | | | |
| | | | |
| | | | |
| | | | |
| | | | |
| | | | |
| | | | |
| | | | |
| | | | |
| | | | |
| | | | |
| | | | |
| | | | |
| | | | |
| | | | |
| | | | |
| | | | |
| | | | |
| | | | |
| | | | |
| | | | |
| | | | |
| | | | |
| | | | |

*Figure 6.2. Emergency lighting record sheet*

## PROVISION OF FIRE SAFETY INSTRUCTION TO INDIVIDUAL STAFF MEMBER

The instruction shown below has been provided to staff member:

Name: _____ Job title: _____

Date: _____ Duration: _____

Instruction was provided by (insert name): _____

Subjects covered (tick box as necessary):

❏ (a) dangerous materials, hazards and safe practices

❏ (b) how to raise the alarm or action on hearing alarm

❏ (c) calling the fire brigade

❏ (d) plant shutdown/power isolation

❏ (e) location and use of firefighting equipment

❏ (f) escape routes (location, use and keeping clear) and assembly point

❏ (g) assisting evacuation of public and disabled (use and non-use of lifts)

❏ (h) security measures (daily and in event of fire)

❏ (i) safety signs, their meaning and measures to be taken

❏ (j) function of and care with any active or passive fire protection systems

❏ (k) use and importance of fire doors, door closers and release devices

❏ (l) need to report hazards, faults, dangers etc.

❏ (m) particular instructions (describe) related to specific duties...

Comments by instructor and/or instructed:

I confirm that I received instruction on the topics ticked above on the date given.

Name: _____ Signature: _____

(A copy of this record should be placed on the employee's personal record file.)

*Figure 6.3. Staff training record sheet*

## FIRE DRILL RECORD

### Record of fire drills

A fire drill should be held at least once and preferably twice a year and a record kept of every drill.

| |
|---|
| **Date of drill:** |
| Cause of evacuation: (i.e. fire drill/false alarm) |
| Number of staff involved: |
| Optimum evacuation time: |
| Actual evacuation time: |
| Time to completion of roll call: |
| Assessment of drill: |
| Remedial action necessary: |
| Person responsible for drill (print name): |
| Fire safety manager's comments: |
| Name: _____ Signature: _____ Date: _____ |

*Figure 6.4. Fire drill record.*

The type and level of fire safety training that is needed in order to comply with the requirements of either the Fire Safety Order or the Management of Health and Safety at Work Regulations 1999 is fairly basic, and such training should be given to *all* employees. Essentially, it should cover those matters that are to be found on the fire action notice, that is to say:

- what to do on discovering a fire;
- what to do on hearing the fire alarm;
- how to summon the fire brigade.

On the subject of what to do on discovering a fire, all employees should:

- know how to activate a break-glass manual fire alarm call point;
- understand the colour coding systems for portable fire extinguishers;
- know the different classes of fires;
- know the types of extinguishers that may, and may *not*, be used on the different classes of fires;
- know how to use the extinguishers.

Further information on the types, uses and colour coding of fire extinguishers is shown on the inside front cover of this book.

As for what to do on hearing the fire alarm, all employees should:

- be able to recognise the sound of the fire alarm;
- in the case of a two-stage alarm system, be able to distinguish the intermittent (stand-by) signal from the continuous (evacuate) signal;
- understand the importance of closing doors and windows as they evacuate the building;
- know the whereabouts of all the escape routes from the building;
- know the whereabouts of the assembly point(s).

Training in fire alarm recognition may easily be given as part of the induction training for new employees, by playing an audio tape of the alarm sound(s). All new employees should, on their first day at work, actually walk the escape routes from their work area to the appropriate assembly point(s) outside the building.

Although, in larger organisations, it is likely that the responsibility for calling the fire brigade will be assigned to a member of the security or reception desk staff, all staff should know how to perform this simple but very important task. They should be taught that, having dialled 999, they should, when asked which service they require, say 'the fire brigade'. They should then *slowly and clearly* give the address of the premises and, before replacing the receiver, wait for the brigade personnel to read back the address.

This last point is extremely important and can, in the confusion that may well attend the outbreak of fire, be easily overlooked.

## The training of fire wardens

Article 15 of the Fire Safety Order requires the responsible person to:

- establish and implement appropriate procedures to be followed in the event of serious and imminent danger to those on the premises (an emergency plan); and

- nominate a sufficient number of persons to implement procedures to be followed in the event of serious or imminent danger.

In smaller premises with limited numbers of staff this role may be undertaken by the responsible person themselves. However, in larger premises, the appointment of fire wardens/marshals will assist significantly in:

- maintaining good standards of fire safety throughout;

- offering a greater degree of control and hence safety during emergency evacuations; and

- the implementation of other aspects of the emergency plan.

Whether we call these people fire marshals, floor marshals, or fire wardens is of little importance. For the purposes of this chapter we shall, to be consistent with Chapter 7, call them fire wardens.

The content of a suitable course of training for fire wardens will, to some extent, depend upon the nature of their employer's business, but any such course should include detailed instruction on the evacuation procedure to be followed in the event of fire, elementary fire prevention and hands-on training in the use of portable firefighting equipment.

### Duties of the fire warden

The training given to fire wardens should include a short session on the duties and responsibilities that they are, as fire wardens, expected to discharge. These duties, which are outlined in Chapter 7, should be given, in writing, to each fire warden.

### The evacuation procedure

The fire wardens will, as members of staff, already know the importance of shutting windows and doors as they leave the building, the whereabouts of all the escape routes from the building and the location of the assembly point(s). They should also be trained to switch off machinery or equipment prior to evacuation, take any other actons required under the emergency plan and to make sure that their area of responsibility is clear of people before they themselves leave the building.

They should also appreciate the importance of trying to ensure that the evacuation takes place in an orderly fashion, free from undue haste or panic. The fire wardens should also ensure that any special procedures – such as the use of 'evacuation' chairs – for the evacuation of injured or disabled people, are put into effect.

On reaching the assembly point, the fire warden should report to the chief fire warden, or the designated fire safety official, that their area is clear of people. This is by far the best way of ensuring that the premises have been completely evacuated. The older practice of having a roll-call at the assembly point is of little value in a large organisation. The apparent absence of a particular member of staff does not necessarily indicate that they are still in the building; it could be that they were out to lunch, out on company business or simply absent from work on that day. Having ushered their charges to the assembly point, the fire wardens should ensure that they remain there until the fire officer in charge gives permission for staff to re-enter the building.

## *First-aid firefighting*

While training in the use of portable fire extinguishers, fire hose reels and fire blankets may be done by means of lectures and/or the showing of videos, and this may well be sufficient for the generality of staff, for fire wardens there is no substitute for hands-on training in putting out fires. Having actually used all the various types of extinguishing agents, a fire blanket and a hose reel to extinguish fires under controlled conditions will give them the added confidence to tackle a real fire if ever called upon to do so. In any programme of training in first-aid firefighting, the following points should be stressed:

- not to attempt to fight a fire on their own;
- not to let the fire come between them and their means of escape;
- not to continue to fight the fire if it continues to grow or if it threatens to involve containers or cylinders of flammable gases or highly flammable liquids;
- not continue to fight the fire if it has not been extinguished by one extinguisher.

In any training in first-aid firefighting, whether theoretical or hands-on, it is of paramount importance that those being trained are told that they may only attempt to tackle a real fire if they are confident that they may do so without risk to themselves or to anybody else.

## Fire prevention – hazard spotting

There is a further aspect of fire warden training that does not always receive the attention that it deserves; that is fire prevention. While it is undoubtedly true that the prime responsibility of fire wardens is to ensure the safe evacuation of those in their care, and then, if possible and safe to do so, to extinguish the fire, it would clearly be better if they could prevent the fire happening in the first place. A well-tried method of teaching the fire prevention message is to train the fire wardens to spot fire hazards. This may best be done by way of an illustrated lecture showing slides of hazards that may start fires, hazards that may allow the fire to spread once it has started and, most importantly, hazards that would delay or in any way impede the safe evacuation of people in the event of fire.

## Elementary fire science and fire statistics

A basic understanding of the physics and chemistry of fire, coupled with up-to-date knowledge of fire-related statistics, will enable the fire warden to understand why fire doors should never be wedged open, why windows and doors should be closed on evacuating a building, why holes in fire compartment walls should be fire-stopped, why good housekeeping and good security play an important part in fire safety management, and why time is of the essence in a fire situation.

The fire science should include such topics as the elements of the fire triangle, the various mechanisms – convection, conduction, and radiation – by which fires spread, the speed at which fires spread, the toxic nature of smoke, and the temperatures that may be reached inside a building on fire.

The fire statistics could include the numbers of fires per year, the annual toll of fire deaths and injuries and their causes, the principal causes of fires, the statistics of arson and the financial and environmental costs of fires.

Whilst a knowledge of the statistics of such things as financial, job and business interruption losses is not strictly necessary in order to understand the importance of good fire safety practices, it has a place in the scheme of things in that such knowledge will help to reinforce the important message that fire really is a serious threat to the economic life of the country, and that there is therefore a very real problem to be addressed.

## Fire safety legislation

There is one further topic that may, with advantage, be included in the programme of training for fire wardens and that is fire safety legislation. The principal reason for its inclusion is to give them the authority that they need to discharge their important duties. In a sense, fire wardens are always on duty; they have the thankless, and never-ending, task of telling their colleagues that they must not prop open the fire door or remove the extinguisher from the fire point and so on. Almost inevitably they will be regarded by some as officious martinets who have nothing better to do than interfere in other people's business. The chances of them being so regarded is lessened if the warden can explain that it is not a question of his being an awkward, interfering, busybody, but rather a matter of compliance with the law of the land.

The items covered in the fire safety legislation training should include the main provisions of the Regulatory Reform (Fire Safety) Order in England and Wales or other legislation relevant in Scotland or Northern Ireland.

## Training for fire safety managers

Article 18 of the Fire Safety Order requires the responsible person to appoint one or more competent persons to assist them in implementing or undertaking the preventive and protective measures identified as necessary through the fire risk assessment process. Although there is at present no legal requirement to train those charged with the overall responsibility for the management of fire safety within an organisation (which may include the responsible person), there is a strong case to be made for more specialised and in-depth training for such personnel particularly when considering the requirement for such individuals to be 'competent'. They will be responsible for the selection, purchase, installation, testing and maintenance of various fire safety systems – fire detection and alarm systems, sprinkler systems, emergency lighting, computer suite protection systems etc. Clearly, they can hardly be expected even to begin to discharge these heavy responsibilities unless they have a good overall understanding of the construction, and the principles of operation, of these various systems.

To give but one example of the sort of problem that might well land on the fire safety manager's desk: his employer decides that the company should install the very latest fire detection system throughout its various factories and asks for the manager's recommendations. In such premises, there will be production areas, warehouses, office accommodation, kitchens and canteens etc. Does he recommend point detectors or line detectors? Smoke detectors, heat detectors, or flame detectors? If he needs smoke detectors, should they be optical detectors or ionisation detectors? Where should he go for help? Unless he fully understands the principles of operation of these various options, he will be unable to appreciate why a particular type of detector is the one of choice for a particular application and will, as a consequence, be unable to make recommendations that are both sensible and cost-effective. Furthermore, unless he has the necessary knowledge of the subject, he will, in such circumstances, be at the mercy of any unscrupulous salesman or fire-safety consultant. The way to equip the fire safety manager with the necessary knowledge is to subject him to an in-depth course of training.

Fire safety managers will also be responsible for the installation and/or replacement and maintenance of fire doors and fire-resistant glazing. These all-important items of passive fire protection can easily be rendered all but useless by installers and maintenance contractors who have little or no knowledge of the factors that determine the integrity and effectiveness of such elements of construction. If he is effectively to oversee and control the activities of such personnel, the fire safety manager will need to have a thorough knowledge of the various standards and codes of practice that govern the selection and installation of fire doors and fire glazing.

From time to time fire safety managers may be involved in the planning of structural alterations to their premises and, if they are to ensure that the planned alterations do nothing to compromise the fire safety of the premises, they will need a good overall knowledge of that part of the Building Regulations (Schedule 1, Part B) that deals with fire safety in new and altered buildings, and its interpretation in Approved Document B, *Fire safety*. They will also need a more thorough understanding of relevant British Standards and fire safety law, including how to carry out a fire risk assessment, as is required by the Regulatory Reform (Fire Safety) Order 2005.

A further responsibility of the fire safety manager will be the appointment and training of fire wardens and therefore they must themselves be fully conversant with the topics covered in the fire warden training programme.

There remains one more area of fire safety for which the fire safety manager should assume responsibility; that is the safety of operations involving hot work.

The statistical record of fires started by contractors and others engaged in processes such as welding, cutting and grinding is such that it is essential that all activities involving hot work should be controlled by a hot-work-permit system. It is often the fire safety manager who will have the responsibility for designing, issuing, and monitoring compliance with hot-work permits and, therefore, he or she, will also need thorough training in the specific dangers associated with the various types of hot work, and the recommended contents of the hot-work permit.

Finally, bearing in mind the highly technical nature of subjects in which the fire safety manager is to be trained, and the speed with which innovations in fire safety are introduced, it is extremely important that the fire safety manager is kept abreast of the latest developments by attending refresher courses and seminars and conferences on particular aspects of fire safety.

# The role of the fire safety manager

Legal responsibility for complying with the Regulatory Reform (Fire Safety) Order 2005 lies with the 'responsible person'. As described in chapter 2, the 'responsible person' is defined as meaning 'the employer, if the workplace is to any extent under his control' or, where this does not apply, the occupier as 'the person who has control of the premises' or the owner 'where the person in control of the premises does not have control... of a trade, business or other undertaking'.

In practice, every company should have a director, or senior manager who is responsible for fire safety and has this remit written into his or her job description. To manage fire safety on a day-to-day basis, however, the task is normally delegated to an individual known as the fire safety manager. This role may be, and often is, combined with other duties such as health and safety, environmental management or security.

## The fire safety manager

In order to prevent loss of life and protect property in an emergency and to draw attention to potential fire safety problems in the workplace the fire safety manager should appoint a number of fire wardens (sometimes known as floor wardens) who, in turn, should each have deputies. In large companies, the fire safety manager may also be responsible for the occupational fire brigade.

The fire safety manager should in response to the findings of the fire risk assessment:

- appoint fire wardens and deputies by name;
- designate an area of the premises for which each fire warden will be responsible;
- specify the fire wardens' duties in writing;
- establish procedures to enable the fire wardens' reports to be actioned;
- train the wardens and their deputies in their duties;
- maintain continuity when staff who are fire wardens are on holiday, leave the company or are moved to other areas;

- control the issuing of hot-work permits (see Chapter 6);

- liaise with the local authority fire brigade.

The fire risk assessments required under the Fire Safety Order will, in most companies, be an additional task for the fire safety manager. As stated elsewhere in this book, this is not a 'one-off' project but one that requires revisiting regularly.

When the initial risk assessment has identified the hazards and the means to combat them a decision should be taken about what additional fire precautions may be necessary. The fire safety manager should draw up a plan to ensure, as far as reasonably practicable, the life safety of everyone on the premises from all foreseeable causes of fire; and the protection of the company's premises, assets and records to ensure the continuing viability of the business.

A written fire precautions policy should be prepared and implemented with regard to:

- establishing a fire safety management structure, including designating those people responsible for each part of the plan;

- action to eliminate or reduce hazards wherever practicable;

- monitoring unavoidable hazards;

- preventing the spread of smoke and flames;

- ensuring the safety of all staff and visitors;

- enforcing the fire precautions;

- training staff in the actions they should take in the event of fire and how to recognise, remedy and report fire hazards;

- precautions against the disruption of business;

- other measures to reduce possible losses which, in turn, might attract savings in insurance premiums.

These measures will have a bearing on the emergency procedures which deal with the action to be taken if a fire occurs (see Chapter 10). When the policy has been prepared it may be appropriate to check the risk assessment in the light of any additional fire precautions that have been taken.

## Liaison with the fire brigade

The fire safety manager also has an important role to play in liaising with the fire brigade. If there is an occupational fire brigade there are many benefits in carrying out joint exercises with the local authority brigade. Inviting the crews from the local fire station to familiarise themselves with the layout of your premises can be very beneficial if a fire were to occur. In large buildings, plans should be made available to the fire brigade on their arrival. It is common practice to provide these in a box adjacent to the fire alarm panel.

In the case of large sites, the fire brigade should be informed of any roadworks that are being undertaken on site that may affect fire brigade access, temporary obstructions such as scaffolding that may obstruct firefighting operations and any work that may affect availability of water supplies.

## Liaison with others

The fire safety manager should also liaise with the company security manager. This is especially important with regard to fire exits as there is a possible conflict of interests in that security considerations will demand as few final exits as possible, whereas the fire safety requirements often seek more than this number.

Escape routes may need to be established for use, in an emergency, through areas that otherwise have to be kept secure. Where this involves hardware such as electric locks that are linked to the fire alarm so as to release doors when a fire alarm call point is activated, or on failure of the mains power supply, procedures for testing the equipment will have to be agreed with the security manager.

There will also need to be close co-operation with the security manager with regard to postal devices and bomb threats where the fire wardens may have important roles to play in evacuating all or part of the building and undertaking searches. (See Chapter 8.)

Where fire escape routes pass through neighbouring property or across the land of the adjacent premises, close liaison should be maintained with the fire safety manager of the company next door in order to ensure that the escape routes are maintained clear of obstructions and to become familiar with the means by which the exits are fastened. Contact with the neighbouring premises should also be made when fire drills are planned so that staff may use these routes. Again this liaison may involve your security manager and/or the security manager of the neighbouring premises.

# The role of the fire warden

The principal duties of the fire warden are to:

- take appropriate and effective action if a fire occurs;
- ensure that escape routes are available for use;
- identify hazards in the workplace;
- record and report their observations.

If a fire is discovered, the fire warden should:

- ensure that the alarm has been raised;
- check that manufacturing processes have been made safe;
- evacuate staff from the building or area involved;
- check that any staff or visitors with disabilities are assisted as planned;
- call the reporting centre and give details of the location, severity and cause of the fire, if known;
- fight the fire if it is safe to do so.

When the evacuation signal is heard, the fire wardens should ensure that everyone leaves the area as quickly and orderly as possible, ensuring that security measures, such as closing fire-resistant safes, are undertaken, if this can be done without causing a significant delay in the evacuation procedure. Electrical equipment should also be turned off and windows shut if possible.

When the area for which the warden is responsible has been evacuated, a rapid, methodical search should be undertaken to ensure that no-one remains in storerooms, toilets and similar areas.

The warden should then go to the assembly point and take part in the roll call procedure there. It may be the task of the fire warden or security officer to ensure that no-one re-enters before a fire brigade officer gives permission.

All fire wardens have an important role to play in the fire risk assessment. Any changes to work practices or modifications to existing processes may introduce unforeseen problems. Similarly, changes in procedures may result in the introduction of additional sources of ignition or different types of combustible materials. Any hazards that may be perceived should be reported to the fire safety manager who should consider them, in the light of the fire risk assessment, at the earliest opportunity.

*Figure 7.1. Fire action notice.*

## Fire and bomb drills

Fire drills should be held at least once, and preferably twice, each year. However, drills may be held at different frequencies as determined by the fire risk assessment. Following the fire drills, the fire safety manager should hold a short debriefing session with the fire wardens in order to learn of any problems or difficulties that were encountered. The problems and any remedial action taken to reduce their occurrence in the future should be recorded. Fire drills are important exercises and provide an opportunity for plans and procedures to be developed and modified if necessary.

In some premises where there is a risk of terrorist action directed towards the premises or to others in the vicinity, it is also valuable to carry out a bomb drill occasionally, with the purpose of reminding staff of the actions that they should take. Again, a record of the exercise should be kept and procedures modified if necessary. (See Chapter 8.)

Particular consideration should be given to the actions taken in respect of a device thought to be in the street outside, as well as those to be taken if a bomb were to be placed inside the building.

| Daily | In the morning: | Are escape routes clear? Are the fire exits available for use? |
|---|---|---|
| | In the evening: | Is the electrical equipment switched off? Has rubbish been disposed of safely? Are all windows shut? |
| Weekly | Do self-closers on the doors operate correctly? Are fire signs visible? Is there sufficient space between stored materials and sprinkler heads, fire detectors and lights? | |
| Monthly | Are all extinguishers in their correct places and do they appear to be in working order? Are the hoses on the hose reels neatly coiled and the valves easy to turn on? | |

*Figure 7.2. Sample checklist for fire wardens.*

### Fire action notices and procedures

Proprietary fire action notices such as that shown in Figure 7.1 are entirely suitable for the majority of premises and in very small businesses may be all that is required in the way of an emergency plan. Several variants of these notices are available and care should be taken to ensure that those chosen are appropriate for the building concerned. The blank areas of the notices, such as the location of the assembly area, should be completed, even if these details have already been circulated to staff. Where the proprietary notices are unsuitable, alternatives should be prepared. Fire action notices should be displayed prominently throughout the premises; in practice they are often displayed next to each fire alarm call point.

As already indicated, in many small companies little further action need be taken in respect of emergency plans as long as employees receive regular fire safety training and the contents of the fire action notices are explained to them. Care should be taken with staff who do not speak English as their first language, when a translation of the fire action notice should be made available and should be handed to the staff in question. There may be some premises where it would be advantageous to display fire action notices in alternative languages as well as in English. This may be particularly valuable where there may be a significant number of visitors who speak foreign languages.

Fire action notices should be inspected regularly to ensure that they remain in position, are legible and have not been defaced.

Large companies, those with special security provisions and those with a high fire risk rating may require procedures to be written down as a basis for staff instruction and to be handed to relevant personnel. Even in some smaller companies some staff who have special duties to perform in the event of fire, such as receptionists, cooks and maintenance workers, should be handed written instructions as to what actions are required of them in an emergency.

These instructions should be as clear and concise as possible and be completely unambiguous. If the instructions, lists of fire wardens, areas of responsibilities, shutting down procedures and so on are put together in the form of a manual for the benefit of the fire safety manager, only those sections relevant to a person's fire safety role in the company should be issued to any one member of staff. This not only makes for good economics, it should be remembered that the more writing that is given to a member of staff, the less likely it is to be read.

Each fire warden should draw up a checklist for their area (see Figure 7.2).

# The threat from arson and terrorism

Arson, or wilful fire raising, as it is known in Scotland, is a very old but, until recently, comparatively rare crime. In the 1950s the threat from arson was very remote indeed and less than 0.5% of all fires were set maliciously. The incidence of arson increased dramatically towards the end of the twentieth century but has slowed down recently, although some 20% of fires in dwellings and over 40% of fires in other buildings are still recorded as being started deliberately each year.

In a similar way, there has been a marked increase in terrorism during the past few decades. Fires and explosions have been linked with anything from nationalist and political organisations to several groups of animal rights campaigners, as well as groups with grudges against pregnancy termination clinics, court buildings, military establishments, meat delivery companies, pharmaceutical companies and fast food outlets. Because there is such a wide spectrum of businesses that are potential targets for arsonists and terrorists, or may be affected indirectly by such an event, it is important that all companies take effective action against such threats.

## Bomb attack

In the past, in industry and commerce, there was little reason to justify substantial precautions against bombs. While government departments and the military (in particular) have been on the alert since the 1970s, there were comparatively few attacks on the private sector. The change in terrorist tactics to softer targets has latterly seen the focus shift to shopping centres, transport and the financial sector. At the same time, other 'terrorist' groups have tried to promote their particular causes by targeting activities of which they disapprove; in the case of the animal rights groups, the preferred weapon has been the incendiary device which has been more of a nuisance than a major threat (although such a device destroyed a large, unsprinklered department store).

Experience shows that even if your business has not been specifically targeted by a terrorist group, it may suffer damage from a device left in a town centre. No premises can therefore be regarded as being safe and so fire safety and security managers must all plan and rehearse the actions to be taken both in the event of a relatively small device being planted inside their premises and a much larger object, such as a car bomb, being placed outside.

## Arson

Arson is more commonplace and in some ways is more problematical to tackle. In the past we might not have worried too much about such incidents when talking about business in general but times have changed. Half of all very large fires (that is to say fires each causing damage valued at over £250,000) are thought to be the result of arson. The potential problems of arson tend to be all the problems of accidental fires plus the problems associated with intruders.

It should be noted that the factors which reduce the severity and impact of an arson attack (good security and good fire protection) also have an impact on other risk reduction activities, including the protection of premises from bombs and incendiary devices. Arson fires tend to be larger and more costly because they are started under ideal conditions:

- fuel such as petrol may be brought into the premises to assist the fire;
- multiple seats of fire may be lit;
- plenty of ventilation may be provided by leaving windows and doors open;
- the fires may be lit in vulnerable areas of the building;
- attempts may be made to sabotage fire protection installations.

Where attention is paid to reducing the risk of arson, accidental fires may also be reduced in size and severity.

Basic security measures, such as those outlined below, are effective against arson attack. It should be remembered that arsonists like to work under the cover of darkness and so this form of crime is more likely to occur during winter months and at night time.

## Where the incidents occur

One of the most common forms of arson attack is to push burning materials or pour flammable liquids through the letter slot. This can be countered by providing a sheet metal container to catch the incendiary materials. Proprietary devices are available which incorporate a fire extinguisher which operates automatically in the event of a fire occurring in the container.

The risk of arson is particularly high where:

- the building is in an inner-city area;
- the building is close to a large local authority housing estate;
- the building is near a football ground or similar premises that draws large crowds;

- the building is in an isolated area;
- the locality is known to have a high rate of criminal activity;
- the area is due for redevelopment or has a large number of empty premises;
- there is a high rate of unemployment in the area;
- the locality has experienced a higher than average number of fires.

In the case of explosive devices, a form of risk assessment can be undertaken to determine the likelihood of an attack occurring. As an example, consider a mythical organisation based in a city centre; in this case we could construct the following scenario:

Plus points:

- the organisation has no direct links with government;
- there are no diplomatic, national tourist or airline offices nearby;
- there is no involvement with pharmaceuticals, medical research or the meat trade;
- the building is not shared with other more vulnerable organisations.

Minus points:

- the building is close to a railway station;
- the building is within 250 yards of a street market;
- a political activist group has offices nearby.

From the plus points it is clear that the organisation or its building are unlikely to be primary terrorist targets. The minus points indicate that there is a possibility that the organisation might suffer as a result of collateral damage from a bomb detonated to attack other targets.

Of course, this sort of simple assessment has limited validity when considering some of the attacks that have happened over recent years. Many of these have had a 'random' element to them, where the purpose appears to have been the death of as many people as possible rather than an attack on a specific business.

## Risk reduction and protective measures

Having identified that there exists a real threat, the next stage is to try to reduce the risk factors. Firstly, could the functions be relocated? Does the organisation have to be where it is currently located? This may seem a little drastic but should always at least be considered; in the case of a threat of flooding, for example, it may be that relocation would be the *only* option.

# Case history: Failure of automatic roller shutters assist fire spread

Fire broke out in the haberdashery department of a large department store late one evening as a result of an incendiary device being introduced during opening hours.

A smoke detector operated and the alarm was immediately sent to the fire service control. At about the same time a passer-by saw flame burst from a third storey window and telephoned the fire service.

The fire spread rapidly through the open-plan sales area and reached the fourth floor by way of the escalator well. The roller shutter fitted to protect the escalator failed to operate but the reason for this could not be established after the fire because of the extent of the damage. Once the flames had reached the fourth floor they were fuelled by large stocks of foam-filled furniture.

## Security improvements

This is probably the first thought that will occur, but the impulse to rush out and buy-in expensive security hardware should be resisted until a proper evaluation has been undertaken.

The principles of good security are relevant here, except that they should be aimed at preventing bombs being introduced rather than preventing property from leaving the premises.

The locations most frequently used for planting covert devices are:

- lavatories;
- wastebaskets;
- under or down the side of furniture;
- inside garments on display;
- on external window ledges.

Where premises are attacked more overtly, for example in the case of some arson attacks, then the method or location is less relevant, but the security precautions against any intruder should be adequate to deter or delay the bomber.

Reference should be made to the local police crime prevention department or to your insurers or brokers if assistance is required in determining the sort of security measures that might be appropriate. To summarise, these are:

- security lighting, which can be particularly cost effective against arson attacks;
- perimeter security;
- access control and the screening of visitors;
- surveillance and response to intrusion.

## Reducing the risk by design

In the case of defence against arson, bombs and terrorist attack, there is a great deal that can be done to 'design out' security weaknesses. Many of the improvements suggested below can really only be implemented at the design stage of a building, but others can be implemented as part of a plan of upgrading or rebuilding. Any organisation which considers itself to be a particular terrorist target must take specialist advice when building works are being considered.

The following are features that should be considered:

- fixed automatic fire protection, such as a sprinkler installation;
- the elimination of recesses in which adults or children may loiter unseen;

- segregation of the building from public roads;
- strict control of access to basement areas and car parks;
- elimination of external access to utility areas and plant rooms, minimisation of access points (without compromising fire escape routes);
- segregation by distance from vehicle parking areas;
- modification to reduce the amount of glazing at ground and first floor levels;
- a reception area with ease of surveillance and limited access to the rest of the building;
- sloping sills on external windows;
- modification of external walkways to eliminate blind spots.

As already mentioned, the matter of location is important. When consideration is being given to the choice and layout of a site for a new building, in the case of a company which considers it may be at risk from attack, the following points are worthy of discussion:

- selection of a site which is in an area unlikely to be the scene of public disorder;
- planning the layout of buildings to avoid hollow squares or structures at right angles to each other;
- avoiding covered parking areas and similar places which might attract groups of young people;
- design to incorporate security features noted previously.

Careful thought also needs to be given to the landscaping of the site and the selection of plants and shrubs. Plants of a suitable height which have prickles or thorns have a proven security value.

## Management action

Whatever protective measures are taken, there can be no guarantee that an attack will not have an impact on any particular building or premises. It is essential that all organisations should prepare detailed plans (including plans to deal with evacuation and searching) to deal with the effects of any attack. In addition to the points made in Chapter 10, the plans should cover:

- warning staff and evacuation to the street or to a refuge or shelter area;
- the need for a clear desk policy to minimise loss of documentation should an explosion occur;

- staff vigilance in the post room;

- staff training, particularly in search techniques;

- regular review of the likelihood of attack and of the procedures that have been put into operation.

## Evaluation of threats

Several terrorist groups have discovered that the threat of terrorist action can create as much disturbance as carrying out a real attack, but without the associated risks. Telephoned threats also often attract media attention giving the terrorists the publicity that they desire. There have therefore been a number of hoax threats, some even incorporating recognised code words

One of the hardest things a manager is ever likely to be called upon to do is to give advice on whether or not to take a bomb threat seriously. The decisions made on the receipt of a threat or warning can have profound legal, social and financial implications.

Experience suggests that individual organisations are likely to receive bomb threats from three possible sources:

- from the terrorist directly;

- from the terrorist via the media;

- as a warning from the police.

(The question of government bodies is not dealt with here as they have their own arrangements for evaluating and disseminating information about likely attacks.)

Many incendiary attacks take place after warnings have been given, but the threat or warning is often passed to a third party such as the police or media. 'Genuine' threats (those that include a known code word or phrase) must always be acted on, even if they are only the latest in a long line of false alarms.

Although incendiary attacks may take place after warnings have been given it should be remembered that devices may have been planted in your premises hours or even days before.

If written warnings are received the letters should be handled as little as possible and should be passed to the police immediately.

If a telephone call is received, the switchboard operator or other recipient of the call should write down:

- all that is said by the caller, particularly noting any code words used;

- whether the caller is male or female, adult or juvenile and their mental and emotional state;

- any accent, dialect or slang that is spoken;
- any background noises which might indicate where the call came from.

Ask questions as to:

- the size, appearance and position of the device;
- who is calling;
- when the device will activate;
- why the attack will take place.

Equipment can be purchased which automatically records telephone calls coming into the premises. Calls may then be replayed by security staff and police investigators.

The person receiving the call must be aware of the telephone procedure, which should instruct the recipient to report immediately, and confidentially, to a designated member of senior management. This will prevent panic and allow contingency plans to be put into operation.

Immediately call the police. Inform the security staff so that areas of the building may be evacuated if the threat is thought to be credible. Consideration should be given to introducing additional security measures or personnel if it is thought that such action may prevent a threatened attack.

A form such as that shown in Figure 8.1 may be used to gather information during a telephone call.

## Responses

The following outline procedure should satisfy the majority of circumstances:

- response to telephone threat by person receiving the call;
- evaluation of threat by senior management;
- initiation of plan by appropriate person;
- possible options:
  - evacuate without searching,
  - search without evacuation,
  - partial evacuation and search,
  - ignore.

## CHECKLIST FOR TELEPHONISTS

**Action to be taken on receipt of an incendiary or bomb threat**

- Do not put down the handset or cut off the call.
- Obtain as much information as you can.
- Try to keep the caller talking for as long as possible.
- Complete the information below asking questions in sequence if necessary.
  - Identity or code word _____
  - Message (exact words) _____
  _____

  - Where is it? _____
  - What time will it go off? _____
  - What does it look like? _____
  - What kind of device is it? _____
  - Why are you doing this? _____
  - Who are you? _____
- As soon as the call is complete, note the time and inform a member of staff in authority immediately.
- Complete the following details as soon as practicable, adding anything further that you recall.

- *Details of caller:*
  man ☐
  woman ☐
  child ☐
  old/young ☐ _____
  not known ☐

- *Distractions:*
  noises on the line ☐ _____
  call box pay tone or pips ☐ _____
  operator interruptions ☐

- *Speech:*
  intoxicated ☐
  rambling ☐
  irrational ☐
  impediment ☐ _____
  laughing ☐
  serious ☐
  accent ☐ _____

- *Other noise:*
  anyone in background ☐ _____
  traffic ☐
  talking ☐
  typing ☐
  machinery ☐
  aircraft ☐
  music ☐
  children ☐

- *Message:*
  read ☐
  spontaneous ☐

- *Number on which call was received:*
  _____

- *Person receiving call:*
  _____

*Figure 8.1. Bomb threat checklist (from* An Introduction to Physical Security Techniques, *S. Kidd (ed), Loss Prevention Council, 1996).*

## The police

There are a number of points which must be made clear. The response of the police to a bomb warning will vary from location to location according to the nature of the warning and the operating procedures of individual forces. It may be that, in some areas, the police will respond without delay and help to assess the credibility of a particular threat. They will often be able to give advice on whether the building should be evacuated, but normally the decision to evacuate will be a matter for the management concerned.

Searching premises is also a matter for the company or organisation although again, in some areas, police may be able to assist or provide advice.

Premises or organisations considered to be high risk targets would be well advised to seek police input into their plan at the earliest opportunity. Police crime prevention officers are a good point of contact and may be able to arrange for an appropriate specialist to attend meetings and get involved in the formulation of the plan.

## Searching

The searching of a large or complex building is not a task to be undertaken lightly and thus the decision to mount a search must be taken at an appropriate level.

There are two types of search: the routine and the specific. Routine searches would be carried out when a particular threat was thought to exist. For example, if a generalised warning has been issued by the police that a bombing campaign is likely. In this case, a search should be made of vulnerable parts of the building at the end of each working day. Particular attention should be paid to areas to which the public or visitors have had access.

When a specific threat is received, the search team should be tasked to cover the same areas but in much more detail and possibly under police control.

The best people to search an area are those who know it best; such people are clearly in an ideal situation to identify items that are foreign to the area. This is why if a partial evacuation is to take place, those staff leaving the building should be told to take their personal belongings with them (the opposite of what should be done for a fire evacuation). This reduces the burden on the searchers. Search procedures should include the following:

- identification of objects or materials which are not immediately recognisable;
- closing and marking doors, racks or aisles when searching has been completed;
- sweeping up rubbish and where possible placing it in the metal bins with lids.

Searching the building can be a particularly onerous task especially, for example, in large retail premises. Searches may be of a routine nature or in response to a threat.

At the end of each day a search of those parts of your building accessible to outsiders should be made, especially if a group which may threaten your premises is known to be active. To ensure that the search is more than a cosmetic exercise, the staff involved must be utilised effectively and complete the task thoroughly. The procedure should include:

- searching particularly vulnerable areas where devices may be hidden, such as

  ◦ the pockets of hanging garments,

  ◦ down the sides of armchairs,

  ◦ beneath furniture and fittings,

  ◦ toilets accessible to the public;

- identifying objects or materials which are not immediately recognised by those who work in the area;

- closing and locking all windows and doors when the search has been completed;

- sweeping up all rubbish and emptying rubbish bins into a metal container with a metal lid.

When a threat has been received, action will be co-ordinated by the police, but in most instances essentially the same plan that has been practised for searching at the end of the day may be utilised.

If a device is thought to have been found during a search, *it should not be handled in anyway whatsoever*. If the police are not already in attendance they should be called immediately and they will make arrangements for the device to be made safe. Some suspect packages may have to be left in position by the police until a military examination can be made. All parts of the device will then be removed by the police for a detailed forensic examination.

## Action to be taken if a suspicious object is found

If a suspicious object is found, *it should not be touched or handled in any way*. If police are not already at the scene they must be called. Police control will make the necessary arrangements for the suspect item to be dealt with. The following points should be borne in mind:

- the room containing the suspect item must be secured but should not be locked;

- radios should not be used in the vicinity;

- lights already on should be left on but other lights should not be switched on;

- windows in the area should be left open, if possible;

- a sketch map of the location of the device and a brief description should be prepared for the use of the unit tasked to deal with it;

- ensure that the areas around, above and below the device are evacuated and report this fact to the police.

## Evacuation

One of the most frequently asked questions in this whole subject is 'Are there circumstances when evacuation of a building can do more harm than good?' It is certainly true that there are cases on record where a building has been evacuated following a warning only for some of the occupants to be killed or injured when a bomb planted *outside* the building exploded.

It is this uncertainty that makes the whole problem one of the most difficult likely ever to be faced by a manager. By evacuating a building you expose staff to potential harm during the actual evacuation itself; heart attacks among those walking down many flights of stairs are not unknown. Staff outside the building are vulnerable to the weather as well as devices planted in cars or waste bins.

If at all possible, staff or other occupants should be evacuated to a safe location. This could be the building core away from the windows (but make sure that the core is constructed of material which will provide protection against blast) or it could be a basement. Here mutual aid schemes can work well. For example, two large stores near each other could enter into an agreement that if one has to evacuate its staff (for any reason), then the other store will make its staff canteen available as a reception area. This sort of scheme costs nothing and is worth exploring. Alternatively, sports centres, schools or church halls may also provide safer assembly areas than the street.

A distinction between fire evacuation and a bomb evacuation is drawn elsewhere and it is important that the differences are fully understood, particularly with regard to the removal of personal property, coats, cases and bags which is essential in a bomb evacuation. There is also a need for shutting doors and windows in a fire evacuation, whereas they should be left open in a bomb evacuation. Because of the differing responses required from staff, the fire alarm should not normally be sounded in the case of a bomb alert. An alternative system, perhaps utilising the public address system or a voice alarm installation, should be used.

## Staff awareness training

It is essential that any programme of security improvements or emergency preparedness includes the requirement to provide staff awareness training. All security measures depend on staff co-operation and participation; when breaches of security occur it is inevitably as a result of human error.

Many organisations have found that the existing fire warden/fire marshal structure lends itself well to being adapted to deal with bomb procedures. Fire wardens, who should know their areas thoroughly, may be easily trained to carry out searches or lead search teams.

## Incendiary devices

Incendiary device is a term used to describe any one of a wide range of improvised devices used to start fires deliberately. They are frequently employed by activist groups as a means of drawing attention to political, moral or religious issues and are occasionally used to attack individuals or families. The devices vary considerably in sophistication and effectiveness and it is essential that proper vigilance is maintained by any potential target, particularly when extensive media coverage of an attack may result in 'copy-cat' activity.

Incendiary devices can vary in size from large to small, and be sophisticated or amateur in their design. They can consist of up to five parts:

- a timing mechanism, which may be mechanical, chemical, or electrical;

- an ignition source which may also be mechanical, chemical or electrical;

- a primary fuel, normally a solid material;

- a secondary fuel; liquid, solid or occasionally gas;

- a container to hold the components, although parts can be tied or taped to the outside.

The so-called 'petrol-bomb', a particular favourite of the urban terrorist at times of public disorder, is a simple device consisting of a container of liquid fuel and a burning wick as an ignition source. Others may be very sophisticated, but postal devices, because of the unpredictability of the postal service, rarely contain a timing mechanism. *No suspect package, however, should ever be considered to be safe to handle.* When activated, ignition may take place explosively, or, if the device is being handled, liquid fuel may drop and ignite clothing. Even a small incendiary device, carefully located, has the potential to kill and injure people; it may also cause immense damage, especially if it actuates in an unoccupied building at night. Larger devices, particularly those incorporating gas cylinders, can cause blast damage on a similar scale to small explosive charges.

# Case history: The value of effective fire protection

In the early hours of a January morning three large retail outlets in Northern Ireland were destroyed by a number of incendiary devices. None of these shops was protected by a sprinkler installation, despite energetic encouragement by the fire brigade. Notice was taken, however, of a demand by the fire brigade that a two-hour rated fire-resistant roller shutter be installed between a DIY store and an adjacent shop, which was fully sprinklered. Following the incident two points were of particular note:

- the terrorists had not targeted the sprinklered building;

- the performance of the fire-resistant roller shutter had been impressive, with the contents of the DIY store on one side totally destroyed, while there was virtually no damage on the other side.

## *Targets for devices*

Targets for incendiary devices will vary, depending on which protest groups are active. Attacks in the past have been made on:

- central or local government buildings;
- offices of political parties and ethnic minorities;
- shops, especially those selling animal furs and skins;
- clinics specialising in abortion;
- laboratories thought to be carrying out experiments on animals;
- military establishments;
- legal establishments including court buildings;
- printers thought to be producing inciting material;
- offices of extremist groups;
- newsagents thought to be selling foreign subversive literature;
- food premises thought to be environmentally or hygienically unacceptable;
- homes in rural areas used primarily for holidays, cars outside them and agents selling such houses;
- manufacturing or processing plants thought to be damaging the environment;
- fast food establishments;
- retail premises operated by racial minorities.

Individuals may also be targeted. In the past, attacks have been made on people thought to be associated with:

- the Government or Civil Service;
- the law;
- military operations;
- political parties;
- radical political groups;
- strike-breaking and industrial action;
- vivisection and exploitation of animals;
- abortions.

These lists are not exhaustive and the possibility of further protest groups being formed to demonstrate a real or imaginary grievance against your business should always be borne in mind.

## How a device enters the premises

Devices can enter the premises by a number of routes:

- *Through a window or skylight.* Petrol bombs are often used to commit arson and so measures should be taken to guard against such a device being thrown through the windows of premises at night. Your precautions should also prevent fireworks, flares and similar items starting fires within your buildings.

- *Letterboxes.* Petrol bombs or timed devices may be dropped through a letterbox; on occasion these are supplemented with volumes of flammable liquid. It is therefore advisable to consider fitting a sheet metal container behind the letter slot to retain any flammable liquid or package and prevent flames spreading further into the premises.

- *Brought in by visitors.* Proper security measures should be taken when premises are closed and also during daylight hours, particularly in premises open to the public. Visitors may give the impression of being in the building on legitimate business or, in the case of retail premises, may appear to be customers. Devices they introduce will invariably incorporate some form of delay mechanism, but if they are brought in during working hours they will most probably be quite small and therefore easy to hide, especially, for example, in a department store. Effective devices can be made small enough to fit in a cigarette packet, matchbox or audio/video cassette cases.

- *Sent through the post.* Devices sent through the post are often aimed at a particular individual in the organisation, rather than the company. This type of device rarely has a timing mechanism; actuation occurs as the package is opened. To avoid disruption to the smooth running of the business, the 'post room' is best sited in such a position that it may be evacuated rapidly and without the need to evacuate other large areas of the premises.

## Recognising a device

Incendiary devices can take many forms, and considerable problems can arise in identifying them because they can so easily be camouflaged. They may be disguised to appear as a piece of litter, for example a cigarette packet, or a product on display, such as an audio or video cassette.

Many incendiary attacks are made by sending a package through the post. Clerks, secretaries and post room workers should be vigilant when receiving any package which is more bulky than a normal letter and their suspicions should be aroused if:

- the package is inordinately heavy for its size or is unevenly weighted;
- wires or electronic components are protruding from the envelope;
- greasy or sweaty marks are present on the wrappings;
- the package has a smell similar to that of marzipan or almonds;
- the name and address is in obviously disguised hand-writing, or in cut out or stencilled letters;
- the postmark indicates the package has been sent from an area associated with past incendiary attacks;
- the postmark is foreign, particularly from an area from which you are not expecting mail;
- the package appears to contain a book which is unexpected;
- the package bears an excessive number of stamps;
- the envelope has been addressed to an individual by job title rather than by name and is marked 'personal' or 'private';
- the flap is completely stuck down either with additional adhesive or tape;
- the package is received in a padded envelope, particularly if a staple or staples have been used to reinforce the sealing flap at the top or bottom.

## Action to take

If a lit incendiary device has been thrown into your premises, or if a fire has ignited possibly as the result of an attack:

- sound the fire alarm;
- call the fire brigade and the police;
- evacuate the premises;
- do not attempt to fight the fire;
- alert the fire safety manager to the possibility of an incendiary attack having occurred;
- warn any other branches of your business.

**BEWARE: If one device has ignited others may be present on your premises.**

If you have been threatened with an incendiary attack:

- inform the police;
- inform your security staff;

- if a specific threat is made, consider the need to evacuate the relevant part of the building whilst it is searched;
- consider taking further security measures as appropriate.

**BEWARE: It is dangerous to assume that the threat is a hoax.**

If you think you have located a device hidden in your premises:

- it should not be touched or moved; it may contain anti-handling devices;
- immediately inform someone in authority;
- evacuate the building or area in which the package was found leaving a clear route to the device, with doors left open;
- any lights that are on should be left switched on, but do not turn on any lights that are off;
- call the police and fire brigade;
- write down a description or drawing of the device and its location to hand to police on their arrival, but do not stay near the package to do so;
- security and other radio transmitters in the area should not be used.

**BEWARE: Devices hidden in buildings often contain timing mechanisms which cause ignition during the night.**

If you think you have received a device in the post:

- do not attempt to open it;
- place it on a dry flat surface, if possible in the open air;
- do not cover it with sand or any material;
- do not place it in water;
- do not bend, squeeze or shake the package;
- evacuate the immediate vicinity;
- call the police and fire brigade.

**BEWARE: The device may be a bomb rather than an incendiary.**

If, when you have partly opened a package you suspect it to be an incendiary:

- do not open it further;
- do not attempt to reseal it;

- do not remove the contents, or cover the package in any way;
- lay it down carefully on the nearest flat surface;
- evacuate the office or working area.

**BEWARE: If any solid or liquid chemical spills out of the package:**

- wash areas of skin and clothing with which it may have come into contact with copious quantities of water;
- if liquid squirts into the eyes wash with large amounts of water immediately and obtain urgent medical attention;
- materials dropping loose onto a table top or the floor should be left in position for police examination.

## Be prepared

If your business is one of those which may be the subject of an incendiary attack, it is important that:

- you develop a plan to deal with both the possibility and consequences of an attack;
- staff are aware of the possibility of attack and are trained accordingly;
- because of the inadvisability of fighting fires resulting from incendiary devices, consideration should be given to the installation of:
  ◇ automatic fire detection systems,
  ◇ automatic fire extinguishing systems, such as sprinklers.

The installation of a visible closed circuit television system throughout the building may have a deterrent value. If this is equipped with a remotely located recorder, the tapes should be made available to the police if an incident occurs.

This chapter has been compiled with the aim of providing a basic plan to deal with an incendiary or bomb attack or threat of an attack. This basic plan may need to be adapted for your organisation, and further guidance should be sought from your local police force.

# A simple fire risk assessment

This chapter presents a simple form of risk assessment that may be used by owners or managers of small companies where an elaborate or quantified form of risk assessment as described in Chapter 3 is not appropriate. The questions may also be used as a checklist by managers of larger premises.

The answers to all the questions should be 'yes' (or 'not applicable'). If the answer to any question is 'no' then steps should be taken to rectify the deficiency as soon as is practicable. When the work is complete the fire risk assessment should be reviewed to ensure that the measures taken have not compromised any other part of the plan.

## STAGE 1: IDENTIFYING THE FIRE HAZARDS

| | |
|---|---|
| 1. Is there a system for controlling the amounts of combustible materials and flammable liquids and gases that are kept in the work place? | yes/no/not applicable |
| 2. Is the system operating effectively? | yes/no/not applicable |
| 3. Are all combustible materials and flammable liquids and gases stored safely? | yes/no/not applicable |
| 4. Are all heaters fitted with suitable guards and fixed in position away from combustible materials? | yes/no/not applicable |
| 5. Are all items of portable electrical equipment inspected regularly and fitted with correctly rated fuses? | yes/no/not applicable |
| 6. Is the wiring of the electrical installation inspected periodically by a competent person? | yes/no/not applicable |
| 7. Is the use of extension leads and multi-point adapters kept to a minimum? | yes/no/not applicable |

| 8. Are flexes run in safe places where they will not be damaged? | yes/no/not applicable |
|---|---|
| 9. Is the upholstery of furniture in good condition? | yes/no/not applicable |
| 10. Is the workplace free of rubbish and combustible waste materials? | yes/no/not applicable |
| 11. Is there a designated smoking area provided with adequate ashtrays? | yes/no/not applicable |
| 12. Have suitable measures been taken to protect against the risk of arson? | yes/no/not applicable |
| 13. Have measures been taken to ensure that smoke and flames cannot spread from one compartment within the building to another? | yes/no/not applicable |

## STAGE 2: IDENTIFYING THE PEOPLE WHO COULD BE AT RISK

| 14. Is there a sufficient number of exits of suitable width people present? | for the yes/no/not applicable |
|---|---|
| 15. Do the exits lead to a place of safety? | yes/no/not applicable |
| 16. Are gangways and escape routes free from obstructions? | yes/no/not applicable |
| 17. Are the escape routes free from tripping and slipping hazards? | yes/no/not applicable |
| 18. Are steps and stairs in a good state of repair? | yes/no/not applicable |
| 19. Are final exits always unlocked when the premises are in use? | yes/no/not applicable |
| 20. Are the devices securing final exits capable of being opened immediately and easily without the use of a key? | yes/no/not applicable |
| 21. Are internal fire doors labelled as such and normally kept closed? | yes/no/not applicable |

| 22. Are the self-closers on fire doors operating correctly? | yes/no/not applicable |
|---|---|
| 23. Do the doors on escape routes open in the direction yes/no/not applicable | of travel? |
| 24. Are escape routes clearly signed? | yes/no/not applicable |
| 25. Are escape routes adequately lit? | yes/no/not applicable |
| 26. Have plans been made and rehearsed regarding assisting disabled staff and visitors to evacuate the premises? | yes/no/not applicable |
| 27. Do any staff work alone or in remote parts of the premises? | yes/no/not applicable |

## STAGE 3: ELIMINATE, CONTROL OR AVOID THE FIRE HAZARDS

| 28. Do procedures and practices avoid the use of combustible materials or processes that use heat? | yes/no/not applicable |
|---|---|
| 29. Has consideration been given to all cost-effective measures that could be taken to prevent the occurrence of arson? | yes/no/not applicable |
| 30. Have staff been trained in how to call the fire brigade, the use of the fire extinguishers and basic fire prevention? | yes/no/not applicable |
| 31. Have you asked your insurers for advice regarding the fire protection of your premises? | yes/no/not applicable |

## STAGE 4: CONSIDER WHETHER THE EXISTING FIRE SAFETY PROVISIONS ARE ADEQUATE OR NEED IMPROVEMENT

| 32. Where escape lighting is installed, is it in working order and maintained regularly? | yes/no/not applicable |
|---|---|
| 33. Is the fire alarm system in working order? | yes/no/not applicable |
| 34. Is the fire alarm tested weekly? | yes/no/not applicable |

| | |
|---|---|
| 35. Can the fire alarm be raised without placing anyone in danger? | yes/no/not applicable |
| 36. Are the fire alarm call points clearly visible and unobstructed? | yes/no/not applicable |
| 37. Is an adequate number of suitable fire extinguishers provided? | yes/no/not applicable |
| 38. Are fire extinguishers and fire blankets located suitably and ready for use? | yes/no/not applicable |
| 39. Are the fire extinguishers serviced annually by a competent company or person? | yes/no/not applicable |
| 40. Is any fixed firefighting installation or automatic fire detection system in working order? | yes/no/not applicable |

## STAGE 5: RECORD THE FINDINGS

| | |
|---|---|
| 41. If you employ five or more people have you recorded the findings of the fire risk assessment? | yes/no/not applicable |
| 42. Have you told your staff or their representatives about your findings? | yes/no/not applicable |
| 43. If you have prepared a formal report has this been shown to your staff or their representatives? | yes/no/not applicable |
| 44. If you share the premises with others do they know about the risks that you have identified? | yes/no/not applicable |
| 45. If you do not have direct control over the workplace have you made your findings known to the owner or landlord? | yes/no/not applicable |

## STAGE 6: PREPARE AN EMERGENCY PLAN

| | |
|---|---|
| 46. Are fire action notices displayed prominently throughout the workplace? | yes/no/not applicable |
| 47. Has an emergency plan been drawn up in case of a major fire? | yes/no/not applicable |
| 48. Is a copy of the emergency plan kept other than at the workplace? | yes/no/not applicable |

## STAGE 7: CARRY OUT A PERIODIC REVIEW OF THE ASSESSMENT

| | |
|---|---|
| 49. Has a procedure been established to review the fire risk assessment periodically? | yes/no/not applicable |

A more comprehensive fire risk assessment is set out in Appendix B.

# Planning for emergencies

To stay in business after disaster strikes requires careful pre-planning, you will not be able to sort things out on the day. To overcome a disaster, and the spiral of impact which will follow, requires a plan; a small business can often make do with a plan written on one piece of paper but larger or more complex organisations will have more comprehensive arrangements. There is no universal solution. All organisations, however big or small, will need to go through the same basic process to produce their plan.

To most companies the principal non-natural threats are from fire, burglary, vandalism or terrorist action. Serious storms, floods or water escape from other sources can also have a major impact, especially if premises are in low-lying land near a river and essential machinery, stores, or computer equipment are sited on the lower floors.

By not planning to deal with such threats, businesses, staff and shareholders are exposed to quite unnecessary risks. Planning makes a substantial difference to the possibility of surviving an incident. Indeed any organisation which undertakes a logical, structured view of the threats facing it and then works out how to respond to them has already reduced the impact if disaster strikes.

If the company also trains and exercises staff in implementing the plan it has an excellent chance of surviving the disaster and recovering.

Having made a comprehensive survey of your premises and organisation, and taken action to correct any weaknesses found, the next step is to start to plan how you would respond should an incident occur. This plan is essential so that in an emergency you have a good idea of what you will do in the early stages of recovery. All experience tells us that what we do in the first few hours dictates just how well we will survive.

## Business continuity plans

While it is impossible to predict every kind of possible incident that may threaten a company, it is relatively easy to establish a basic plan which can be implemented to cover a wide range of possible emergencies or disasters.

# Case history: The value of having an effective disaster plan

In the evening of Friday, 10 April 1992 a terrorist bomb seriously damaged the headquarters of a large insurance company. Because a comprehensive emergency plan had been drawn up, by Monday morning furniture, computers, telephones and supplies had been delivered to a relocation address and over 500 staff were at work. This could not have been done without careful planning, which had been tested by exercises, and as a result jobs were preserved and the business has continued to flourish.

The basic principle of any business continuity plan is that it will provide a framework for an organisation to fall back on in a crisis. Developing a shelf full of plans for specific emergencies, and nothing more, runs the risk that the emergency which does occur is the one that was not foreseen, or that an anticipated emergency develops in ways that had not been foreseen, with the effect that the specific plans are of limited assistance or are even rendered useless.

The starting point must be the development of flexible management arrangements for handling a crisis, whatever its cause. It therefore follows that the crisis management arrangements should align with normal management arrangements, not least because routine activities will have to be maintained while the emergency is handled.

This integration of routine and business continuity plans and procedures embraces a number of concepts, all of which need to be amalgamated in your organisation if they are to be truly effective. There are four main areas where this integration must take place:

- First, the principal emphasis in the development of any plan must be on the correct response to the incident and not to the cause of the incident. (Although this principle would not prevent an organisation developing a fire team which could start to fight a fire while other employees are initiating a salvage plan.) The plan has to be flexible; it has to work on bank holiday weekends or in freezing weather conditions. It has to be clearly written and easily understood. All involved must clearly understand the part they have to play. It will need to be regularly tested against specific circumstances. This will require an assessment of the hazards faced by your organisation and consideration of the adequacy of the planned response in each case.

- Second, any emergency management arrangements must be integrated into your company's structure. Emergency plans must build on routine arrangements and it is therefore essential for those who will be required to respond to any emergency to be involved in the planning process. This sounds like commonsense. However, all too often independent groups develop plans for an organisation which are only dusted off after the incident has occurred, by which time it is too late and that absolutely crucial immediate response is less than effective.

- Third, the integration of the activities of different departments or divisions within your organisation. The overall response to a crisis will invariably need input from a number of different departments. Effective planning must integrate these contributions in order to achieve an efficient and timely response to an incident. Not to be aware of the contribution to be made by other sections within a company is a recipe for a muddled response.

- Fourth, the vital need for you to look over the wall and coordinate arrangements with your neighbours and other authorities who might become involved (such as the police or fire brigade) and consider how local implementation of the Civil Contingencies Act 2004 may impact (see below). It is obvious that, to achieve a truly coordinated and effective response, you and your neighbours must know each others' capabilities, such as the use of each others' emergency equipment, temporary secure storage and so on.

Before finally starting to draft your plan you should define the functions which are critical to or irreplaceable in the continuity of your business, for example, information on computer systems such as customer details, current order book information, supplier information, staff information, specialist tools, equipment and stock, manufacturing drawings, legal documents and so on. You will also need to identify the minimum staff needed to maintain a service to your customers whilst recovery from disaster is under way. Finally, you will need to define the length of time you can afford for recovery to take place as this will shape your recovery plan, determining, for example, whether or not relocation of part or all of your facilities is needed.

Remember to keep a copy of the plan and its associated documents, such as lists of telephone numbers, *off* the site to which it refers.

Although all plans are different they will all have a number of features in common. The following paragraphs will serve to act as an aide-memoire and will also be useful as a skeleton to help you if you have to draft a plan from first principles.

## The business continuity plan

The introduction to the plan should cover:

- the clear purpose of the plan, bearing in mind that it is better to allocate a definite time frame for the recovery of critical functions than to rely on a general statement of intent;

- a clear statement of support by the board of directors and/or senior management team;

- a description of the premises, facilities and operations covered by the plan and an outline of activities or processes carried out in the premises;

- the main hazards faced by the business and the effect these hazards could have on the business;

- the structure of the team(s) responsible for managing the recovery. Team leaders (and in bigger organisations a deputy) should be nominated and each member will normally have an identified function such as facilities, information technology, rescue of pre-designated items of value, supplies, public relations and so on.

## Counter terrorism

At a time of heightened awareness and when central and local government are radically revising arrangements for emergency planning and response, it is vital that business plays its part in improving resilience across the board. Does your business or its products make you particularly at risk from terrorism; does your location – in a city centre, for example – make you vulnerable to denial of access to your premises following an event, even though they may not be directly damaged? The implementation of appropriate measures will help reduce the risk from terrorist action and improve the resilience of your business. In any event, you should consider the following:

- *Manage staff securely:* take up references, request proof of qualifications, verify the identity of new employees before confirming a job offer.

- *Manage contractors securely:* use only established, reputable contractors; investigate contractors' processes for validation of staff; institute procedures involving passes and photographs to identify the persons working at your premises; agree procedures for substituting temporary replacements when the usual staff are unavailable.

- *Ensure that staff are aware of procedures* to be followed in the event of a bomb warning or other threat at the premises, in the surrounding area or in the event of an instruction from the emergency services to evacuate the premises. These issues are discussed in greater detail later in this chapter.

## Implementation of the plan

It must be made clear *when* business continuity plans are to be implemented and *who* has the authority to implement them. This authority is not necessarily related to seniority or status. Often the decision to put emergency procedures into effect will have to be taken outside normal working hours. If a fire occurs at 0300 hr on a Sunday morning security personnel should not have to ring up the chief executive to seek permission to call out the fire brigade! Thus the plan must clearly indicate under what circumstances it should be implemented. Key points for inclusion here are:

- when and how to implement the plan;
- the persons responsible for initiating its implementation;

# Civil Contingencies Act 2004

This piece of legislation came into force on 14 November 2005; its purpose being to establish a consistent level of civil protection across the UK and improve its resilience in the face of new challenges in a post 9/11 world. It modernises outdated legislation (from the 1920s and 1940s).

The Act identifies Category 1 responders including police, fire and rescue services, ambulance, maritime and coastguard agencies and local authorities. Category 2 responders include utilities, railway and airport operators, harbour authorities and the Health and Safety Executive (HSE). Category 1 responders are core organisations which are likely to be involved in dealing with most incidents. Category 2 responders are defined as key co-operating bodies which are less likely to be involved with the heart of planning work, but will be heavily involved in incidents which affect their particular sector.

There are four main civil protection duties that fall on Category 1 responders under the Act:

- risk assessment;

- business continuity management;

- emergency planning; and

- maintaining public awareness and arrangements to warn, inform and advise the public.

A fifth duty applies to local authorities alone:

- promotion of business continuity management to the commercial sector and voluntary organisations.

Category 1 and Category 2 responders also have a common duty to cooperate and share information to help ensure a robust and joined up approach to emergencies.

As referred to above, an important step in the development of any plan, particularly for larger organisations, will be to 'look over the wall' and in particular have discussions with the local authority to ascertain what measures may already be in place that have the potential to affect your plan and conversely how your own plan may affect or have influence on wider scale emergency plans for your area or region.

- the delegation of authority for specific functions, e.g. removal of specified items to a pre-planned place of safety or calling out pre-arranged specialist support;

- call out lists of key personnel, which must of course be kept up to date;

- the designation of either an on-site office or an off-site incident centre, such as a hotel or another business, with appropriate communication facilities (telephones, fax etc) to act as a focus for the management of the response to a disaster and recovery from it.

## Call out and check-off lists

Call out lists, giving names, positions in the organisation and contact telephone numbers, form a key part of all plans and are critical to their success, particularly during the crucial early stages of the response. It is essential that such lists are updated regularly, at least monthly. Those individuals with key roles to play, such as members of the recovery teams, should be supplied with simple check-off lists of the actions they must take on being told of the incident. These lists should be readily available at all times – in cars, at home and in the office. Taking the correct action during the early stages of the response is absolutely crucial, and check-off lists can usefully list the actions which you would expect to be taken in, say, the first three hours of the response, the next 12 hours etc.

## Salvage and damage control

The plan should set out the means and resources to be used to minimise damage to premises and equipment. It should specify the location of salvage equipment and detail the names and telephone numbers of those trained in its use. Details of possible sources of assistance should be included, for example:

- experts in the salvage of documents and data held on IT systems and computers;

- smoke residue removal experts;

- plant hire contractors for pumps, generators or heating equipment;

- experts in decontamination (if appropriate);

- points of contact for all the utilities (gas, electricity, telephones, water) and local authority engineering services;

- points of contact for any national authorities which might be involved such as the National Rivers Authority if rivers might be polluted as a result of the incident;

- transport and removal companies;

- building contractors, architects, and structural engineers;

- insurers or brokers as appropriate.

First-aid firefighting methods can be extremely effective if executed early, but misuse of extinguishers and other equipment can cause great harm and put people at risk; for example, use of the wrong type of extinguisher on an electrical fire. In larger buildings or complexes serious consideration should be given to the formation of 'in-house' fire teams and damage control squads. Trained employees can be mobilised rapidly on the sounding of the fire alarm to extinguish or contain a small fire before the fire brigade arrives. They can also check that the evacuation of the building is complete and that all doors have been closed to minimise the rate of fire spread. The fire brigade should be consulted about the setting up of these teams and can give advice on training. The fire brigade also need to be aware of any formal arrangements that may result in employees continuing to work inside a building after part of it has been evacuated.

The information available for salvage and damage control teams (staff, volunteers or fire brigade) should include separate details for each room including lists, in priority order, for items to be removed or protected, particularly those items which are irreplaceable, such as works of art. It may be appropriate to include relevant photographs of specific items. Members of the fire teams and salvage squads should be volunteers and must be physically fit. Employers' liability insurance should be checked to ensure that it covers such activities.

Specialist advice should be sought in dealing with water-damaged records and files. This should be done without delay as, for example, combustion products can be highly acidic and, therefore, very corrosive. As an emergency measure, certain valuable items (such as books, but not photographs) can be frozen in commercial freezers. This will arrest further damage until skilled assistance can be obtained.

It should be remembered that work in and around damaged buildings poses very special problems and may be dangerous.

In most areas specialist salvage firms are available and larger organisations may wish to enter into some form of contract with one of these companies.

### Evacuation

If a fire is reported an immediate evacuation should be undertaken. Occupants should leave the affected building and report to a pre-determined assembly point and the fire brigade called. Fire wardens or floor marshals should ensure that all parts of the building have been evacuated and the senior warden must advise the first fire brigade officer whether or not all persons are accounted for.

There will also be other occasions when evacuation of premises may be required, such as in the case of the threat of a fire spreading from neighbouring property or as a result of threatened flooding. Conversely, it may be necessary to keep everyone in a particular building whilst a problem is resolved, such as a bomb or other terrorist threat where the location of the threat is uncertain.

Particular points to bear in mind for an evacuation plan are:

- identification of the people who are authorised to initiate the evacuation plan;

- designated sites where evacuated personnel are to muster;

- designated personnel to be the focus at each evacuation site;

- designated tasks for individuals if they can undertake them safely prior to evacuation, for example:

  ◇ turning off utilities,

  ◇ taking custody of certain items,

  ◇ maintaining the security of the premises;

- transfer of telephone callers to pre-designated locations;

- provision of a focal point for contact by the emergency services and others.

If there is a need to contain people in a building, particularly in the event of an external terrorist threat, plans must be prepared for this and should include:

- designation of a safe area where people should congregate, away from the danger of flying glass;

- provision of telephone facilities in the safe area;

- availability of toilet facilities and drinking water;

- availability of special facilities if old people, children or animals may be involved.

### Relocation

This part of the plan should cover the arrangements which may be needed if the business has to be relocated to other premises. It should include any pre-planning undertaken in acquiring an alternate location as well as details of sources of assistance which may be needed (for example, contacts with estate agents, property companies and local authorities).

Alternatively, arrangements could be made with the providers of disaster recovery suites which offer a range of services including fully equipped, secure office suites with desks, telephones, personal computer and local area network connections, with access to fax, photocopying, toilet and kitchen facilities if required. Additionally most offer an IT mirroring service whereby software and data can be held on remote servers hosted by the disaster recovery suite providers which will enable, following an incident, business critical systems, software and data to be available for immediate use.

## Communications

It is essential that the organisation communicates its plans speedily and effectively to all those with whom it does business, for example:

- employees (who will need to be told what to do);

- neighbouring premises (including homes and housing);

- local authorities, including enforcement bodies;

- customers or clients;

- suppliers;

- shareholders, the stockmarket and banks;

- the media (radio, television and newspapers).

The plan will have to cover not only emergency communications for the immediate aftermath of the disaster (radios and mobile phones – but it should be noted that in the event of a geographically widespread emergency such as flood, the mobile phone networks may be overloaded and service will be unavailable) but also longer term measures, for example having telephone calls diverted to alternate locations, possibly run by a specialist contractor, or diversion of mail to pre-designated premises. Key points to include in the plan are:

- internal and external communications;

- locations of existing facilities;

- sources of supply for additional mobile telephones or two-way radios;

- control of radio communications;

- telephone procedures and duties of switchboard operators;

- assignment of diary/log keepers to ensure proper records of messages and decisions, particularly important for any form of future enquiry;

- the manner in which messages are to be fed to the media.

Electronic media, i.e. the internet and e-mail can be extremely useful communication tools in the event of an emergency. The development of voice-over internet protocol (VOIP) services for use over broadband connections may also prove to be a useful communications tool if normal or mobile telephone systems are unavailable.

Remember also that the media can be swiftly at the scene, reporting what they see to the local community as the incident unfolds. This can create many worried families and so plans must include arrangements for notifying next-of-kin about what has happened. Plans are also needed to ensure that non-involved staff are kept informed and are told about any changes which may affect them.

## *Other support services*

All plans will need to allow for the provision of specialist support and services. These will include such things as:

- data protection and recovery arrangements, for example:

  ◇ procedures for back-up and off-site storage,

  ◇ mutual aid for running software,

  ◇ sources of replacement equipment and software;

- details and data relating to customers and suppliers;

- precautions relating to key plant or equipment, such as:

  ◇ listing their types and specifications,

  ◇ planning methods of protection or replacement,

  ◇ stockpiling or sources of spares or components;

- availability of transport;

- forecast of needs;

- designation of alternate sites for operations;

- manpower and personnel, for example:

  ◇ details of key staff (additional or secondary skills),

  ◇ in-house fire and salvage teams,

  ◇ sources of external assistance and mutual aid;

- security concerns, for example:

  ◇ site protection (including gates and perimeter),

- ◇ reception of emergency services,
- ◇ assigned rendezvous points,
- ◇ management of the media and other visitors,
- ◇ support from local police.

There may be other factors special to your business, and these will become apparent during training sessions and exercises.

## Senior management support and endorsement

The completed plan must be seen to have support at the highest level and a clear statement to this effect must be placed at the beginning of the plan. Without Board or similar support, few line managers will respond enthusiastically to the diversion of resources, which is implicit in developing contingency plans and training to implement them.

## After the incident

The first few minutes following an incident such as fire, flood or explosion are the most significant and any action (or inaction) at this stage can have far-reaching consequences. Just as the correct first aid applied in the immediate aftermath of an accidental injury can save life and promote rapid recovery, so too the correct response can ensure that the effects of an incident are minimised.

Disasters usually cause trauma and stress and long-term psychological support may be needed, particularly if there have been fatalities. This needs to be borne in mind as people recover from the effects of the incident.

After the incident, access to the site may be restricted by considerations of structural integrity or for the investigation of the cause of the incident, which may last for a number of days or even weeks in some circumstances. The structural integrity of the building or its remains must be established as a first priority by specialist advisers and any stabilising measures carried out before other activities can take place on site. If the incident may be the result of a crime the police will require the scene to be preserved whilst evidence is gathered, and this can take hours or days.

A selection of salvage equipment should be kept on the premises, for example waterproof sheets, squeegees, shovels, ladders, ropes, brooms, hard hats, gloves, emergency lighting equipment, heavy-duty plastic sacks and plastic sheeting. Specialist personnel will bring their own equipment if they are invited to assist.

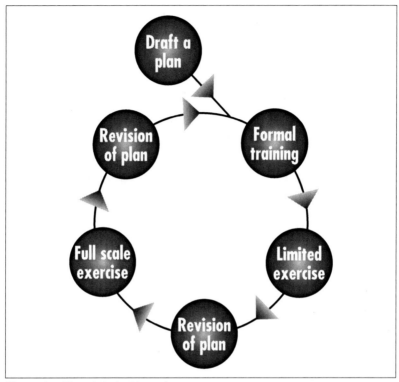

*Figure 10.1. The training/revision cycle*

The plan should include some or all of the following:

- damaged roofs should be covered with tarpaulins in order to minimise subsequent rainwater damage;

- appropriate warning signs and barriers should be erected;

- as far as possible, residual water should be removed using squeegees, cloths and suction equipment. Lift shafts and other sumps will have to be pumped out;

- additional personnel may be needed to assist with salvage, particularly during weekends and holiday periods;

- consideration should be given to the need to plan for suitable, secure storage space for salvaged materials;

- to remove the smoke odour it may be necessary to use a process in which a deodorising liquid is passed through electrically driven sprayers;

- used fire extinguishers should be recharged;
- hose reels should be wiped clean and rewound;
- alarm systems should be reinstated;
- premises should be safeguarded against theft, broken windows should be boarded up and broken doors should be repaired and padlocked;
- the premises may require a manned guarding service.

## Public relations

The public relations part of the plan has to cover a wide range of activities. This will be crucial if the cause of the disaster can be attributable in any way to an act or omission of the organisation. Poor handling of the media has led to the destruction of companies. Skillful handling of the media can go a long way to defusing potentially hostile comment. The fact that a company has clearly taken great care to plan properly will result in less aggressive handling of the incident by the media. Key points to note are:

- the nomination of official spokesmen;
- contact lists of journalists and radio/television stations;
- access to specialist facilities, for example, telephone answering services which may need to be employed in cases of product contamination;
- pre-prepared background facts on the organisation, functions, safety record, personalities etc.

## Training and exercises

One of the most common failings in contingency planning is to prepare detailed plans and then sit back and assume that if the unthinkable does happen everything will be all right. This is a most dangerous and deceptive illusion. A paper plan on its own is worth considerably less than the effort that went into drafting it.

Training of all those who have a role in the plan is essential. This should begin with formalised sessions covering the contents and purposes of the plan until all those involved are familiar with the details. It is then appropriate to hold limited-scale exercises with individuals and groups. Once this has been achieved, at least one full-scale exercise should be held at least every two years, and this could involve the emergency services so that, in the event of a real disaster, they are familiar with your premises and you are familiar with the way they work.

## Revision of plans

Another deceptive and dangerous assumption is the idea that once a plan is written it is complete. Plans require constant reappraisal and revision as flaws and omissions in the plan will always be revealed during exercises. At the same time, changes in organisational structure necessitate regular revision and updating of the plan and, of course, more training. This training/revision cycle can be expressed as shown in Figure 10.1.

## Liaison with the emergency services

It is important to talk to the appropriate officers of the emergency services before they are needed. In the case of very large premises or where dangerous materials are stored it is almost certain that the police and fire service will already have emergency plans to deal with incidents because of statutory requirements. For smaller organisations it is important to ensure that the company disaster plan dovetails with emergency service arrangements.

## Risk management and insurance concerns

It has been traditional to rely upon the existence of insurance to deal with problems that occur. Given sufficient insurance cover, the insurers (and the adjusters appointed by them) will see that the financial compensation is fair. However, both insurers and insured are losers; the insurer finds that losses are mounting and the insured finds that premiums rise to pay for them.

Insurers and brokers are all able to give advice on how losses may be minimised and in some cases discounts may available where insurers consider that their exposures have been improved by the implementation of risk reduction measures. This is particularly true for cover against terrorist attack.

Not all losses can be compensated for by insurance. Although cover against consequential loss can be purchased, what of the customer who either gets no reply from his or her telephone call or finds that the line is out of order in the days following the disaster? What he or she may do is approach a competitor; he or she may be lost to the business for ever. What happens to good trained staff dispensed with temporarily and snapped up by competitors?

Even more relevant in many cases is what happens on the morning after the disaster? Staff are left surveying the wreckage, delivery vans are turned away and no one seems to know what to do or who is in charge.

It is in the interest of the insurer, the insured company and its staff to plan in advance so that the business is seen to be coping in the face of adversity and so that confidence in the company is maintained.

# Corrosive smoke: Planning to minimise the acid damage hazard

Although it is often thought that it is the heat and flames from a fire that pose the greatest threat to life, it is the smoke and toxic gases, such as carbon monoxide, that actually kills the majority of victims. As well as being a threat to life, smoke is also responsible for a great deal of property damage, although in this case it is acidic gases in the combustion products that are responsible.

Acid damage is a potential consequence of all fires in buildings. Added to the destructive effects directly caused by fire, and the toxicity effects to life, smoke can cause post-fire corrosion far from the scene of the fire and the costs involved can be much greater than for the fire damage itself. A relatively minor fire can easily be elevated into a major financial loss.

This chapter highlights the hazard, describes the mechanisms involved and lists the measures that may be taken before and after the fire in order to minimise risk of major disruptions to business activities.

Contingency planning is an essential feature of loss limitation. Properly considered procedures can limit the spread of damage and provide effective salvage of contaminated items.

## What is corrosive smoke and how is it produced?

Under certain conditions materials will burn to produce smoke comprising both gas and particulate matter (soot), each of which can contain corrosion agents (usually acid). In a building, fire the smoke can drift or be positively ventilated through ducts and openings to locations far away from the immediate area of the fire and cause considerable extra damage in places which are apparently otherwise unaffected. The most obvious objects of attack are fine surfaces, and high technology and electronic components, but it is conceivable that other items such as building elements, including rods in pre-stressed concrete, may also be affected.

The contents and structure of buildings often comprise large quantities of plastics, for example polyvinylchloride, polyethlene and polystyrene, with a variety of additives. When involved in a fire, dense smoke and corrosive combustion gases are produced, including (depending upon the nature of the polymer and additives):

- hydrogen chloride (HCl);

- chlorine ($Cl_2$);

- sulphur dioxide ($SO_2$);

- oxides of nitrogen ($NO_x$);

- ammonia ($NH_3$).

The corrosive atmosphere is further enhanced by water vapour produced in the combustion process, by firefighting water and normal humidity. This results in the gases dissolving in the water to produce corrosive liquids such as hydrochloric acid.

## *Polyvinylchloride (PVC)*

Polyvinylchloride (PVC), which mechanically and electrically is an excellent material, is inherently flame-retardant, due to the halogen (chlorine) content, but it decomposes at temperatures between 120°C and 300°C, when acid gases are released.

PVC is a thermoplastic material which is resistant to weathering, moisture, most acids, fats, petroleum hydrocarbons and fungal attack. It is an effective electrical insulator. PVC can readily be compounded by the use of plasticisers, stabilisers, fillers and other modifiers so as to be processed by blow moulding, extrusion, calendering and similar processes. The addition of colouring materials in the manufacturing process enables PVC to be used for the manufacture of a wide range of products, including electrical insulation. When heated more intensely it is inherently flame-resistant, and forms a solid char rather than melting and dripping like most other thermoplastics.

The HCl produced by burning PVC is non-flammable, but is very soluble in water, such as the water vapour produced during the fire and the water used in firefighting operations, to form hydrochloric acid. This acid is very corrosive, and is especially damaging to soft tissues if inhaled, as well as to metal surfaces with which it comes into contact. During a fire the HCl gas can spread with the smoke throughout a building, posing a threat to life and causing extensive damage, especially to the microscopic components of computers and machinery of all types incorporating electronic controls. On some occasions significant corrosion has affected the structure of a building as well as equipment and stock. It is therefore very important that immediate action is taken to decontaminate such items following the fire.

## Bromine and chlorine compounds

Chemicals containing bromine and chlorine are introduced as inhibitors in fire-retardant polystyrene and polyurethane foams which are used widely in many applications. If subjected to a small fire, flames do not propagate in the foam but, at a more advanced stage, decomposition takes place and acid vapours are liberated.

Halons, when used to fight a fire, can also be a source of corrosion, although gaseous halons used in their correct applications in computer rooms are extremely good fire-extinguishing agents. Their main problem is that they break down in the presence of fire to liberate halogenous acids (these are acids which contain any of the halogens – fluorine, chlorine, bromine or iodine). The effect of this is the same as described above: corrosion quickly occurs and the same recovery/reconditioning procedures will be necessary.

## Other materials

Other materials also produce corrosive smoke but tests have shown that almost any smoke, even from apparently innocuous substances such as wood, will attack metals, especially under warm, wet conditions. For example, the sulphur content of bitumen used as a coating for steel can produce acidic fumes. When dissolved in the water used for fighting the fire, sulphuric acid is produced which rapidly damages steel and other materials.

The problem is compounded by the manner in which the material is burnt, for example the physical form of the material, the conditions of excess or restricted air, the burning temperature, the degree of confinement and humidity, all of which may lead to the production of differing chemicals in the fire gases and smoke.

## An ideal material

If such a material could be produced, it would contain halogen bound in the chemical structure for fire-resisting purposes, but retain this halogen within the charred material rather than emit it as a gas.

Some authorities consider that there is already sufficient evidence for halogen-free low smoke plastic materials, which are now available, to be promoted as causing significantly fewer corrosion problems in the event of fire, especially in confined, congested, sensitive areas, such as on board ship, in underground railway systems and in nuclear power stations.

There is also some evidence that fluorine-containing polymers prevent less corrosion risk than those containing chlorine.

# Case history: Corrosive smoke incident

At about 0800 hours workmen at this tool manufacturer ignited a bitumen impregnated roof-covering while carrying out gas cutting operations. The fire spread at high level at first, destroying some 200m$^2$ of roof before involving a stack of cardboard and plastic packaging materials in the warehouse below.

There was a delay in alerting staff as the break glass fire alarm call point, which was operated when the fire was discovered, failed to sound the alarm.

Seventy firefighters were involved at the premises for over 4 days, during which time heat from burning boxes caused the collapse of a further 1400m$^2$ of north light roof.

Despite the fire damage being mainly confined to the warehouse, smoke and fumes spread throughout the manufacturing area. Shortly afterwards etching and rusting of both machinery and work in progress were found and tests showed the presence of chloride.

Most of the machinery was salvageable but this was not possible with much of the work in progress, which was already finished to size and had to be scrapped.

## Identifying the vulnerable areas

The items of electronic equipment most likely to suffer in the short term from corrosion damage, due to fluid films of acid, are the mechanical switches and contacts, where the build-up of corrosion products can prevent mechanisms operating and forms an electrical bridge across contacts. Fine conductors can be severed and circuits broken, or resistance can be introduced and circuits behave incorrectly. Tests have shown that even a chloride deposit of 10 micrograms per $cm^2$ can have an effect on the correct functioning of electronic components, due to small leakage currents.

Non-precious metals such as steel, copper and aluminium are attacked if unprotected. Precious metals used on contacts (gold, silver, platinum), plastics and ceramics are usually unaffected.

General corrosion can occur on many other metallic surfaces but particularly on items for which a fine finish is important, for mechanical or decorative reasons. Modern high precision, advanced technology tools, working to great accuracy, are specially susceptible if pitting by corrosion were to occur. Should machine tools have to be returned to their country of origin for repair, costs would be high.

Hydrochloric acid in contact with concrete sections of the structure of the building will react with the lime to give water-soluble calcium chloride ($CaCl_2$) which can penetrate damp concrete by diffusion. It is therefore theoretically possible for corrosion of the iron reinforcement bars and pre-stressing elements to occur, although it is unlikely to be a major problem with concrete subjected to PVC fire gases (although weakening could occur due to temperature effects).

If Portland cement has been used in the concrete, an insoluble complex compound is formed which effectively stops the progression of the chloride through the concrete. Full scale tests of a building with a PVC fire showed that, on good quality concrete, chloride penetration was not greater than 2mm after a period of one year, and thereafter decreased.

## Building design to prevent smoke spread

Cleaning up after acid smoke contamination is a messy, difficult and fairly expensive task, even if carried out in an efficient manner: some items will be beyond recovery procedures and it is therefore worthwhile taking measures to prevent smoke spread.

Many modern buildings use barriers to contain fire within a certain area. Where smoke damage, regarded separately from fire, is a serious consideration, such barriers must also be designed to prevent smoke spread, in areas otherwise undamaged by fire.

Attention must be paid to:

- *Firebreak doors.* Close fitting is essential; the closing mechanism should operate by smoke detection in addition to a fusible link system.

- *Fire/smoke dampers on air conditioning/ventilation ducting.* These must close automatically, or by a manual system, when smoke is present, in order to prevent smoke being distributed by powered means to other, distant parts of the building. In addition to dampers closing, the fans must be stopped.

- *The use of automatic mechanisms operated by temperature (fusible links)* is unlikely to be satisfactory. These would normally operate at about 74°C, but below such a temperature cool smoke would pass through but not activate the mechanism. The use of dampers operated by smoke-detectors may be sufficient but, in view of the possibility of spurious tripping, there is probably more benefit in installing a remotely-operated system of dampers controlled manually from a central area.

- *Ventilation systems* should ideally be divided floor by floor, and consideration should be given to installing independent power supplies in particularly sensitive areas.

- *Holes in floors, ceilings and walls* such as those for conveying service pipes and cables. Considerable attention is required to sealing against smoke penetration. Smoke will readily travel throughout a building by natural convection.

- *Smoke venting.* It is necessary to consider the measures that the fire brigade might be expected to take in fighting the fire. Firefighters need to clear the smoke from the area they are working in and, in doing so, it is possible that they may direct the smoke to smoke-sensitive areas. This is a difficult problem: the firefighters' primary job is to save life, and property considerations are secondary. Nonetheless, smoke clearance must be anticipated in the design of a building and the fire brigade plan of attack in the event of fire must be taken into account when designing the smoke containment or dispersal measures.

- *The use of smoke vents* can be beneficial if, by venting the smoke outside, further permeation of the building is prevented. It is better that smoke vents are controlled manually by the fire brigade.

- *Materials used in the fabric of the building.* It may be possible to reduce the quantity of PVC and other acid-smoke producing materials used in the building structure and decorations.

- *Contents of the building.* The building contents may cause a particular hazard with respect to acid damage, e.g. PVC packaging materials stored in what would otherwise be an area free from materials that would produce acidic smoke. Such materials could perhaps be stored in an outside area.

- *Electrical supply – busbars.* Electrical busbars become hot in use and can transmit heat to associated PVC coated wiring, which decomposes and evolves HCl gas, even if fire does not result. The PVC covering must be sufficiently cut back, within the constraints of electrical safety, to prevent this.

## Contingency planning for a smoke emergency

The control of smoke and loss limitation from the corrosive and damaging effects of smoke should be an element of the contingency/disaster plan:

- assess the building contents for their vulnerability to smoke damage/acid attack;

- assess the potential smoke-producing elements in the building, especially noting PVC cables and other items;

- consider the use of low-smoke or halogen-free cables in smoke-sensitive areas;

- consider the use of fire inhibitors in construction materials based on aluminium hydroxide or silicate rather than halogens;

- assess the system of fire doors and ventilation dampers for the isolation of smoke-vulnerable areas. Check that the operating cables are adequately protected against fire;

- include in the written instructions for personnel in the event of a fire, actions regarding the operation of ventilation dampers and the closing of doors.

The emergency manager should:

- be familiar with the relative importance of particular areas against smoke ingress; and

- fully understand the smoke precautions plan;

- have the authority to preserve a particular area, perhaps at the expense of others;

- know the names, addresses and telephone numbers of specialist recovery firms;

- be able to summon a crisis committee to assist him;

- liaise with the works/public fire brigade.

The insurance manager should make prior arrangements with his insurers, enabling the company to bring in specialists without delay if an emergency arises.

In some establishments, it may be practicable to train in-house emergency specialists, and keep stocks of corrosion inhibitors and smoke recovery chemicals.

## Interim measures to contain the damage

In the aftermath of a fire, urgent remedial action is required to prevent corrosive attack. Correct action must be taken within a few hours to arrest the corrosion process prior to the commencement of cleaning procedures. The emergency manager must take charge during and following the incident and must be able to decide which areas are worth salvaging, considering the limitation of resources available.

In the first instance, by prior standing agreement with the insurers, the insurance adjusters must be contacted and, preferably with their knowledge, an expert reclamation firm employed. A list of companies specialising in this work may be viewed on the Fire Protection Association website at *www.thefpa.co.uk* by following links to the 'Buyers Guide'. These companies operate a 24-hour emergency service and can be on the site within a few hours, day or night.

The principles of preservation of equipment used by the specialists are:

* removing items to other rooms and drying chambers;

* sealing the area so that no further spread occurs;

* selective spraying with de-ionised water and removing surplus water from the area;

* spraying special protective oils onto surfaces to displace water and form a protective film over sensitive equipment, to exclude oxygen and prevent further deterioration;

* reducing the humidity of the air in the building. This involves sealing all doors, windows and other openings, and using fan-assisted dehumidifiers;

* covering with plastic sheeting and using heaters and dehumidifiers locally.

Once these first aid measures have been taken, the rate of corrosion is checked and reclamation work can then proceed as quickly as possible.

## Recovery procedures

If equipment has been affected by smoke damage, modern techniques of recovery can very often return the equipment to a good usable state, provided that:

- it has not been affected by heat from the fire;
- corrosion prevention treatment has been applied within a few hours.

Despite the blackened and offensive look of the equipment, which may initially give the appearance of a total loss, modern techniques may be able to save it. Experience has shown that electronic equipment can survive heavy soot deposits and some corrosive attack. Reclamation companies will usually be able to give some, limited, guarantee of future performance.

These procedures, although complicated, usually cost only a small fraction (commonly 3-15 per cent) of the value of the equipment and, in most cases of cool smoke contamination, should result in a return to fully acceptable serviceability.

Each of the items involved will be individually dismantled. Soot and acid contamination must be removed. Reclamation specialists have developed non-aggressive techniques using de-ionised water and other suitable fluids.

Reinforced concrete is subjected to mechanical surface cleaning, high pressure washing, lime pasting and drying.

## PVC and low smoke emission cables

In recent years a number of fires have occurred where the losses have been significantly increased by acid damage caused by corrosive smoke produced by the insulation materials on electric cables. This has arisen partially because the IEE Wiring Regulations, and latterly BS 7671: *Requirements for electrical installations* have not instructed the specifier or installer to use any specific type of cable and, in the absence of such advice, general purpose PVC insulated cable has been used in the majority of installations without regard to its behaviour in the event of a fault. This type of cable has also been used for economic reasons. When specifying cable systems it is not only the cost which must be considered, but also:

- propagation of fire along a cable run;
- production of toxic gases which can injure and kill people;
- production of smoke which could obscure the means of escape;
- production of acidic gases which can damage property.

As electrical wiring is to be found in virtually every building the problem is very extensive.

### Existing cables

Cables in common use (see Figure 11.1) tend to have plastic insulation of two types:

- thermosetting, which tends to be hard, brittle and resistant to attack by chemicals and heat; or

- thermoplastic, which is soft and pliable with a resistance to chemical attack, although when heated they may melt and burn with varying degrees of ease.

As well as the many toxic gases and pyrolysis products formed during the burning of plastics such as PVC, the carbon produced is visible as thick, black smoke. While many of these combustion products are a threat to the lives of those trapped or still escaping from a building, it is the acidic components that cause the greatest damage to property. The increasing dependence of commerce and industry on computers has resulted in the installation of a correspondingly greater amount of PVC clad cables to power the equipment, thus compounding the problem should a fire occur.

| POWER CABLES | DATA AND TELECOM CABLES |
| --- | --- |
| Power, control and mains cable | Telephone drop wiring |
| Domestic wiring | Switchboard wiring |
| Industrial conduit wiring | Telephone handset flex |
| Automotive harness wiring | Coaxial cable |
| Domestic appliance flex | Fibre optic cable |
| Mineral insulated copper sheathed cable | |

*Figure 11.1. Types of cables which may be insulated with PVC.*

### Technical requirements of new cables

Some major cable manufacturers have recognised that in many cases, both from life safety and property damage viewpoints, the degradation of PVC cables in fires presents an unacceptable threat. Accordingly, alternative ranges of cables have been developed to offer improved smoke and fume performance. The aim is to produce a cable which:

- is comparable in performance, flexibility and resistance to attack from the environment, to those in current use;

- is free from halogens in its composition (chlorine, bromine and fluorine are the halogens which confer acidic properties to the combustion products);

- releases the minimum of acidic gas when tested to the appropriate standards (PVC typically releases 28 per cent);

- complies with the other standards relating to fire-resistant cables.

Although reputable manufacturers aim to meet the above requirements for low smoke emission cables there are reports of some products being introduced which are not of a suitable standard, principally because there are no formal definitions for terms such as 'limited fire hazard', 'low smoke and fume', 'low toxicity' or 'zero halogen' which are being used to market the products. As indicated above, the key elements in assessing the properties of a cable are:

- fire resistance;

- smoke generation;

- acid gas generation;

- oxygen index;

- toxicity of combustion products.

Some large specifiers and users are now requiring an acceptable performance regarding at least three of these criteria before recognising cables as presenting a limited fire hazard.

The new halogen-free cables still have copper conductors, but these may be insulated with fire-resistant tapes covered by cross-linked polyethylene (XLPE) or a hard grade ethylene propylene rubber (HEPR). The form of construction is shown in Figure 11.2. Some cables have silicon rubber insulation which, in a fire, is converted to silicon dioxide, an electrical insulator. Some brands also incorporate a layer of galvanised steel wire armour.

## Applications

Low smoke cables are now readily available from several manufacturers and may be specified for virtually all power supply wiring, control instrumentation and communications applications if required. Such cables are routinely installed in underground transit system stations and highway tunnels where the public could be at risk. They are also used in power station cable runs where access is difficult and the amounts of insulation present could otherwise result in an extremely disruptive incident.

Low smoke emitting cables have also been specified for high rise towers and many notable public buildings, as well as having military applications.

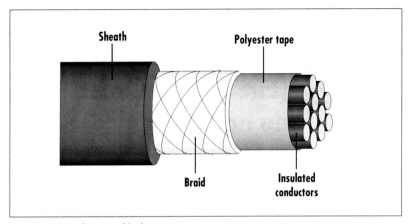

*Figure 11.2. Multi-core cable design.*

When considering installations it should be remembered that PVC has in the past been used in the manufacture of conduits, trunking and ducting. These components are now also available manufactured from low smoke emitting materials, many of which are environmentally friendly in that they may be recycled for future uses if no longer required.

It is important when installing low smoke emitting cables that the correct clips and other fittings are used. The manufacturers' guidance should also be consulted with regard to correction factors for groups of more than one circuit and the minimum bending radius of the cable. Whereas PVC cables may be bent fairly easily, care should be taken not to kink the sheath of low smoke emitting cables; the minimum internal radius of bend of these cables tends to be about 6-8 times the cable diameter.

Although there is now a general awareness of low smoke emission cables with thermosetting insulation, these cables are rated at 90°C conductor temperature and thus the performance of cable accessories such as joints, connectors and terminals must be correctly specified. (The accessories will need to tolerate a short-circuit temperature of up to 250°C.)

Mineral insulated cables should also be considered where appropriate as in some applications unsheathed cables may be used, thereby completely eliminating the use of plastics. Mineral insulated cables are also commonly used for fire alarm and emergency lighting systems where the integrity of a circuit is essential while a fire is in progress.

# Appendix A: Areas where the Regulatory Reform (Fire Safety) Order do not apply

The Regulatory Reform (Fire Safety) Order does not apply in relation to:

- single private dwelling houses;

- an offshore installation within the meaning of regulation 3 of the Offshore Installation and Pipeline Works (Management and Administration) Regulations 1995;

- a ship, in respect of the normal ship-board activities of a ship's crew which are carried out solely by the crew under the direction of the master;

- fields, woods or other land forming part of an agricultural or forestry undertaking but which is not inside a building and is situated away from the undertaking's main buildings;

- an aircraft, locomotive or rolling stock, trailer or semi-trailer used as a means of transport or a vehicle for which a licence is in force under the Vehicle Excise and Registration Act 1994 or a vehicle exempted from duty under that Act;

- a mine within the meaning of section 180 of the Mines and Quarries Act 1954, other than any building on the surface at a mine;

- a borehole site to which the Borehole Sites and Operations Regulations 1995 apply.

*Note that if a disused railway carriage or an old aircraft fuselage was being used as, say, an office, a shop, or a workshop rather than as a means of transport, then that premises would need to comply with the Fire Safety Order.*

# Appendix B: Fire risk assessment checklists

These checklists may be used in conjunction with Chapter 4 to assist in drawing up the risk assessment and emergency plans for your premises. When completing the lists circle or underline the appropriate answers.

## Stage 1: Identifying the fire hazards

*Stage 1a: Identifying sources of ignition*

| | | |
|---|---|---|
| 1. | Does the work activity involve hot processes such as incineration, welding, flame cutting, cooking or the use of ovens? | yes / no |
| 2. | Are there light bulbs and fittings near combustible materials? | yes / no |
| 3. | Are there fluorescent light tubes and fittings near combustible materials? | yes / no |
| 4. | Are portable heaters used? | yes / no |
| 5. | Are there multi-point adaptors in electrical sockets? | yes / no |
| 6. | Are electrical extension leads plugged into adaptors or other extension leads? | yes / no |
| 7. | Are any portable electrical appliances faulty or damaged? | yes / no |
| 8. | Are there any faults with the electrical installation? | yes / no |
| 9. | Is smoking permitted? | yes / no |
| 10. | Is arson a potential problem? | yes / no |
| 11. | Are there any other potential sources of heat in the workplace? | yes / no |

## If so what are they?

If the answer to any of the above questions is 'yes' then go to the checklist for Stage 3a.

### Stage 1b: Identifying combustible materials

The combustible materials that should be considered include those that:

(i)    are used or stored during the business operations;

(ii)   are parts of furniture or furnishings;

(iii)  form parts of the structure or fittings.

| | |
|---|---|
| 1. Do your work processes involve the use of combustible materials such as paper, card or plastics? | yes / no |
| 2. Are bulk quantities of combustible materials (either raw materials, finished goods or waste) kept in the workplace? | yes / no |
| 3. Are large amounts of textiles and furniture (particularly furniture with large amounts of foam padding) displayed or stored in the workplace? | yes / no |
| 4. Are items of furniture damaged with padding exposed? | yes / no |
| 5. Are there large notice boards on escape routes with bundles of loose papers hanging from them? | yes / no |
| 6. Are more than 20% of the walls covered with combustible linings such as hardboard, chipboard, plastic tiles or flock wallpaper? | yes / no |
| 7. Is there any area of the walls covered with carpet tiles? | yes / no |
| 8. Is the ceiling covered with polystyrene tiles? | yes / no |
| 9. Are combustible artificial foliage or plants used to decorate the workplace? | yes / no |

| 10. Are there displays involving combustible materials and panels on escape routes or elsewhere? | yes / no |
|---|---|
| 11. Are paper or similar decorations hung in the building during Christmas or other festival times? | yes / no |
| 12. Are there any other combustible materials in the workplace? | yes / no |
| If so what are they? | |

If the answer to any of the above questions is 'yes' then go to the checklist for Stage 3b.

## Stage 1c: Identifying flammable liquids and gases

| 1. Are stocks of flammable liquids for use in the processes kept in the workplace? | yes / no |
|---|---|
| 2. Are containers of flammable liquids left open, without their tops on? | yes / no |
| 3. Are flammable liquids kept in the workplace for use by the cleaners or maintenance staff? | yes / no |
| 4. Are there quantities of flammable liquids kept for any other purposes? | yes / no |
| If so what are they and why are they kept? | |
| 5. Is natural gas used in a manufacturing process? | yes / no |

| | |
|---|---|
| 6. Are cylinders of flammable gases used or stored in the premises? | yes / no |
| 7. Are cylinders of other gases, such as air or oxygen, used or stored in the premises? | yes / no |
| 8. Are aerosol cans filled or stored in the premises? | yes / no |
| 9. Are there any other forms of compressed gas used or stored in the premises? | yes / no |
| If so what are they? | |
| | |

If the answer to any of the above questions is 'yes' then go to the checklist for Stage 3c.

## Stage 1d: Identifying structural features that could lead to the spread of fire

| A. | |
|---|---|
| 1. Are stocks of raw materials and finished products separated from the workplace by a fire-resistant structure? | yes / no |
| 2. Are the compartments enclosed by a fire-resisting structure? | yes / no |
| 3. Are all holes in compartments walls, ceilings and floors around services such as pipes and cables firestopped? | yes / no |
| 4. Have dampers been installed in ductwork where it passes through compartment walls, floors and ceilings? | yes / no |
| 5. Are holes in the floors and ceilings of vertical service ducts or cupboards firestopped? | yes / no |
| 6. Are all openings in compartment boundaries protected in case of fire? | yes / no |

If the answer to any of the above questions is 'no' then go to the checklist for Stage 3d.

**B.**

| | |
|---|---|
| 1. Are there undivided voids beneath the floor? | yes / no |
| 2. Are there undivided voids above the ceilings? | yes / no |
| 3. Are there voids behind panelling or other features that could lead to a fire spreading to the floor above? | yes / no |
| 4. Are there any other features that could lead to the spread of flames or smoke in the event of fire? | yes / no |

If so what are they?



If the answer to any of the above questions is 'yes' then go to the checklist for Stage 3d.


## Stage 2: Identifying people who could be at risk

| | |
|---|---|
| 1. Do people sleep in the workplace? | yes / no |
| 2. Is there a large number of staff in the workplace? | yes / no |
| 3. Do a large number of members of the public visit the workplace? | yes / no |
| 4. Will people be unfamiliar with the layout of the building and the escape routes? | yes / no |
| 5. Is the workplace used or visited regularly by people whose mobility is impaired? | yes / no |
| 6. Is the workplace used or visited regularly by people with other forms of disability? | yes / no |
| 7. Do people work in remote areas of the premises? | yes / no |

| | |
|---|---|
| **8.** Are contractors and maintenance workers unaware of the dangers posed by fire? | yes / no |
| **9.** Do any staff work in areas where there is a high risk of a fire occurring? | yes / no |
| **10.** Are there any other factors which put people in the building at risk? | yes / no |
| **If so what are they?** | |

If the answer to any of the above questions is 'yes' then go to the checklist for Stage 3.

## Stage 3: Eliminating, controlling and avoiding fire hazards

### Stage 3a: Reducing the risk from sources of ignition

If you have answered 'yes' to any of the questions in Stage 1a, can you:

| | |
|---|---|
| **1.** Replace the work process with one that reduces the potential for ignition? (For example replace a hot work method with one that does not employ flames or heat.) | yes / no |
| **2.** Adopt a hot-work permit system? | yes / no |
| **3.** Reposition light units to reduce the risk of contact with combustible materials? | yes / no |
| **4.** Replace radiant heaters and those employing flames with fixed convector heaters or central heating? | yes / no |
| **5.** Install additional electrical socket outlets? | yes / no |
| **6.** Provide and maintain protective devices such as residual current devices (RCDs) and thermostats? | yes / no |

| | |
|---|---|
| **7. Ensure that the electrical wiring and portable appliances are inspected regularly?** | yes / no |
| **8. Designate an area where smoking is permitted and provide suitable furniture and an adequate number of ashtrays?** | yes / no |
| **9. Provide and maintain appropriate security measures against arson?** | yes / no |

If the answer to any of the questions above is 'no', then go to checklist 3f.

## Stage 3b: Reducing the risk from combustible materials

If you have answered 'yes' to any of the questions in Stage 1b, can you:

| | |
|---|---|
| **1. Replace any of the combustible materials used in the work process with non-combustible alternatives?** | yes / no |
| **2. Reduce the amounts of combustible materials stored in the premises?** | yes / no |
| **3. Store combustible materials in fire-resisting stores or enclosures away from sources of ignition?** | yes / no |
| **4. Reduce the amounts of materials that are being displayed?** | yes / no |
| **5. Replace furniture with combustible upholstery with items which are not so combustible?** | yes / no |
| **6. Replace damaged furniture?** | yes / no |
| **7. Improve housekeeping and the arrangements for the disposal of waste and rubbish?** | yes / no |
| **8. Remove combustible wall linings or replace them with more suitable materials?** | yes / no |
| **9. Remove combustible ceiling linings?** | yes / no |
| **10. Introduce real plants or fire-resistant foliage for decorative purposes?** | yes / no |
| **11. Limit the size of displays and site them away from the main escape routes?** | yes / no |

| | |
|---|---|
| 12. Reduce the size of notice boards and the amount of paper hanging from them? | yes / no |
| 13. Prohibit the hanging of combustible decorations, especially near light fittings? | yes / no |

If the answer to any of the questions above is 'no', then go to checklist 3f.

## Stage 3c: Reducing the risk from flammable liquids and gases

If you have answered 'yes' to any of the questions in Stage 1c, can you:

| | |
|---|---|
| 1. Reduce the volume of flammable liquids that are kept in the workplace? | yes / no |
| 2. Ensure that all containers are kept closed when not in use? | yes / no |
| 3. Replace a flammable liquid or solvent with a non-flammable alternative? | yes / no |
| 4. Reduce, remove or replace the flammable liquids used by cleaners and maintenance staff? | yes / no |
| 5. Ensure that gas-fuelled equipment is serviced and maintained regularly? | yes / no |
| 6. Reduce the numbers of cylinders of flammable and non-flammable gases that are kept in the workplace? | yes / no |
| 7. Reduce the number of aerosol cans stored in the premises? | yes / no |
| 8. Replace aerosol cans, especially those which use butane or propane as the propellant gas, with less hazardous products? | yes / no |
| 9. Ensure that if it is necessary to store large quantities of aerosol cans that they are kept in purpose-built cages? | yes / no |

If the answer to any of the questions above is 'no', then go to checklist 3f.

## Stage 3d: Reducing the risk from structural features

If you have answered 'yes' to any of the questions in Stage 1d, can you:

| | |
|---|---|
| 1. Separate stocks of raw materials and finished products from the workplace by a fire-resistant structure? | yes / no |
| 2. Divide voids beneath the floors? | yes / no |
| 3. Divide voids above the ceilings? | yes / no |
| 4. Firestop hidden areas such as those behind panelling? | yes / no |
| 5. Firestop all holes around services to the same standard as the fire resistance of the element of construction in which they are situated? | yes / no |
| 6. Install dampers in ducts in line with compartment walls? | yes / no |
| 7. Install automatically operating fire-resistant doors or shutters to protect openings in compartment walls? | yes / no |

If the answer to any of the questions above is 'no', then go to checklist 3f.

## Stage 3e: Reducing the risk to people

If you have answered 'yes' to any of the questions in Stage 2:

| | |
|---|---|
| 1. If people sleep in the workplace can you ensure that: | |
| • there is an early warning of fire? | yes / no |
| • that sleeping areas have been evacuated? | yes / no |
| 2. If there is a large number of people present, particularly members of the public, is there a sufficient number of trained staff to ensure speedy and orderly evacuation? | yes / no |
| 3. If the workplace is used regularly by people with impaired mobility: | |
| • is the number of trained staff adequate to ensure safe evacuation? | yes / no |
| • are the escape routes suitable for the people who have to use them? | yes / no |

| | |
|---|---|
| **4. If the layout and the escape routes may not be familiar to the people present:** | |
| • are the escape routes adequately signed? | yes / no |
| • is the number of trained staff adequate to ensure safe evacuation? | yes / no |
| • can instructions and advice be given by a voice alarm or public address system? | yes / no |
| **5. If people present may be unaware of the dangers posed by fire have adequate arrangements been made for their safe evacuation?** | yes / no |
| **6. If people at work are exposed to a high risk of fire have they been trained:** | |
| • appropriately for the hazards? | yes / no |
| • in the action to take in the event of fire? | yes / no |

If the answer to any of the questions above is 'no', the fire safety measures for the workplace need to be re-evaluated before the emergency plan is drawn up.

## Stage 3f: Compensating features

If you have answered 'yes' to any of the questions in Stages 1a, 1b, 1c or 1d, the following compensation features may be considered:

| | |
|---|---|
| **1. In the case of small workplaces, can the work activity be arranged so that any outbreak of fire can be seen immediately by people present?** | yes / no |
| **2. Can an automatic fire detection and alarm system be provided?** | yes / no |
| **3. Can an automatic sprinkler or other suitable fixed firefighting installation be provided?** | yes / no |
| **4. Can a smoke control system be provided?** | yes / no |
| **5. Can the source of ignition be contained by providing fire-resisting walls, doors or shutters?** | yes / no |

# Appendix C: List of useful addresses

**Arson Prevention Bureau**
51 Gresham Street
London EC2V 7HQ

Tel: 020 7216 7522
E-mail:
arsonpreventionbureau@abi.org.uk
Web:
www.arsonpreventionbureau.co.uk

**Association of British Insurers**
51 Gresham Street
London EC2V 7HQ

Tel: 020 7600 3333
E-mail: info@abi.org.uk
Web: www.abi.org.uk

**Association of Insurance Risk Managers in Industry and Commerce**
6 Lloyd's Avenue
London EC3N 3AX

Tel: 020 7480 7610
E-mail: enquiries@airmic.co.uk
Web: www.airmic.com

**Association of Specialist Fire Protection**
Association House
99 West Street
Farnham
Surrey GU9 7EN

Tel: 01252 739142
E-mail: info@asfp.org.uk
Web: www.asfp.org.uk

**British Approvals for Fire Equipment**
Thames House
31 Thames Street
Kingston-upon-Thames
Surrey KT1 1PH

Tel: 020 8541 1950
E-mail: info@bafe.org.uk
Web: www.bafe.org.uk

**British Automatic Sprinkler Association**
Richmond House
Broad Street
Ely CB7 4AH

Tel: 01353 659187
E-mail: info@basa.org.uk
Web: www.basa.org.uk

**British Fire Protection Systems Association**
Thames House
31 Thames Street
Kingston-upon-Thames
Surrey KT1 1PH

Tel: 020 8549 5855
E-mail: bfpsa@abft.org.uk
Web: www.bfpsa.org.uk

**British Standards Institution**
389 Chiswick High Road
London W4 4AL

Tel: 020 8996 9000
E-mail: cservices@bsi-global.com
Web: www.bsi-global.com

**Chief Fire Officers' Association**
10-11 Pebble Close
Amington
Tamworth
Staffs B77 4RD

Tel: 01827 302300
E-mail: enquiries@cfoa.org.uk
Web: www.cfoa.org.uk

**Fire Extinguishing Trades Association**
Thames House
29 Thames Street
Kingston-upon-Thames
Surrey KT1 1PH

Tel: 020 8549 8839
E-mail: feta@abft.org.uk
Web: www.feta.org.uk

**Fire Protection Association**
London Road
Moreton in Marsh
Gloucestershire GL56 0RH
Tel: 01608 812 500
E-mail: fpa@thefpa.co.uk
Web: www.thefpa.co.uk

**Institution of Fire Engineers**
London Road
Moreton in Marsh
Gloucestershire GL56 0RH

Tel: 01608 812 580
E-mail: info@ife.org.uk
Web: www.ife.org.uk

**Royal National Institute of the Blind**
105 Judd Street
London WC1H 9NE

Tel: 020 7388 1266
E-mail: helpline@rnib.org.uk
Web: www.rnib.org.uk

**Royal National Institute for Deaf People**
19-23 Featherstone Street
London EC1Y 8SL

Tel: 020 7296 8000
E-mail: informationline@rnid.org.uk
Web: www.rnid.org.uk

# Index

Lightning Source UK Ltd.
Milton Keynes UK
UKOW041421300113

205604UK00001B/2/P